Read Aloud

Celebrate!

Can you guess my favorite date?
It's any time we celebrate!
Birthday, wedding, New Year's day,
Time to dance, time to play!

Family visit, family vacation,
Each is a special celebration!
Win a ball game? Get a part in a play?
Let's celebrate! Hip hip hooray!

What's the very next holiday date?
Plan a good way to celebrate!
Join a parade! Sing a song!
Celebrate loud! Celebrate strong!

You can make any day great—
When you take time to celebrate!

Name all the celebrations
illustrated on this page.

THINK!   What other days do you celebrate?

Home Letter

Dear Family,

For the next few weeks, we will be talking about different kinds of celebrations. Your child will also be learning about consonants that appear at the beginning, middle, and end of words, as in these example words.

 valentine

 balloon

 butter

Your child will also be learning about the hard and soft sounds for the letters c and g, as in these example words.

 gold

 circus

 orange

At-Home Activities

Here are two activities that you and your child might like to do together.

▶ Ask your child to name the celebration that he or she looks forward to the most. Then ask your child to write a letter to you, telling why this celebration is important.

▶ Make a mobile to celebrate your child's favorite day! Have your child cut out pictures from old magazines, back them with scrap cardboard, punch a hole in the pictures, and tie them to a coat hanger with string. Hang the mobile in a special place.

Book Corner

To extend the unit theme, you may wish to read these books with your child.

Happy Birthday
by Lee B. Hopkins

This anthology of poems spotlights various kinds of birthday celebrations.

Lizzie Logan Gets Married
by Eileen Spinelli

When Lizzie's mother decides to marry, Lizzie decides to take charge.

Sincerely,

▶ Say the name of each picture. Write the consonant that stands for the sound you hear in the middle of each word.

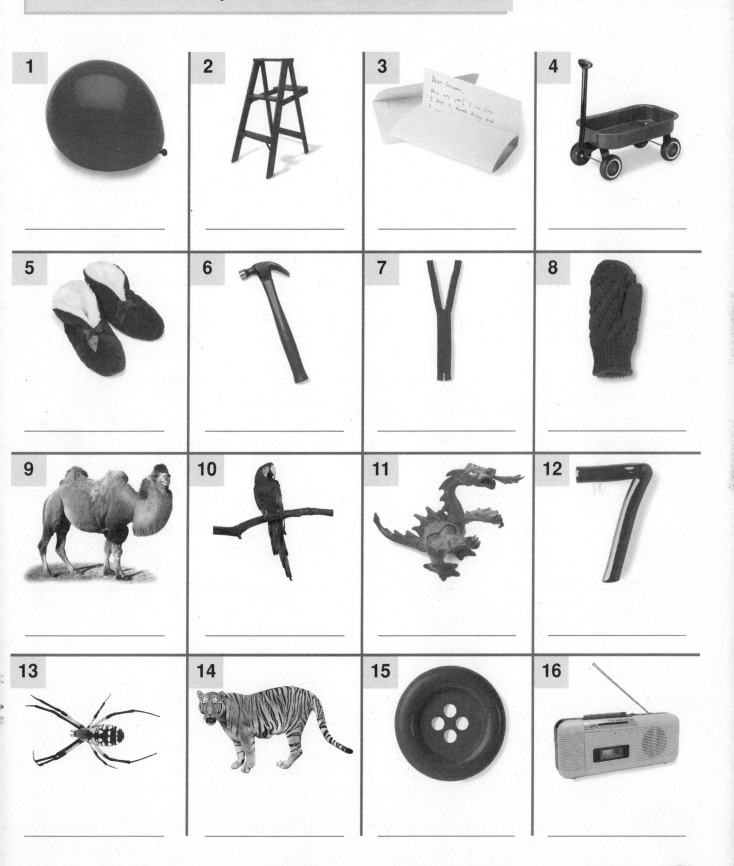

1

2

3

4

_____

_____

_____

_____

5

6

7

8

_____

_____

_____

_____

9

10

11

12

_____

_____

_____

_____

13

14

15

16

_____

_____

_____

_____

Lesson 2
Medial consonants

7

Look at the picture. Read the sentence. Circle the word that will finish the sentence. Write the word on the line.

1 Mom took my _____ sister and me to the zoo.

baby   bunny

2 The zoo is by a park in our _____.

cousin   city

3 First we saw a _____ at the zoo.

tiger   tulip

4 Then we came to the pond where the _____ lives.

honey   beaver

5 Next we saw a big cat called a _____.
It had lots of spots!

leopard   lemon

6 After that we saw a _____ beside a cactus.

lizard   peanut

7 I got to ride on a _____.

parrot   camel

8 As we left, my sister was _____ good-bye
to the animals.

waving   wagon

THINK! What other animals could you see at the zoo?

Lesson 2
Medial consonants

Home   Ask your child to identify the middle
consonant in the answer words.

Name _____

 Look at the letter in each row. Then say the name of each picture. Color the pictures whose names end with the sound of that consonant.

1

t

2

k

3

p

4

x

5

l

Look at the picture. Fill in the circle beside the word that will finish the sentence. Write the word on the line.

1 Ben rides the _____ to school.
- ○ bug
- ○ bud
- ○ bus

2 He likes to wear his red _____.
- ○ cat
- ○ cap
- ○ car

3 Ben takes his lunch in a _____.
- ○ bat
- ○ bad
- ○ bag

4 Today he has a _____ sandwich.
- ○ ham
- ○ hat
- ○ had

5 Ben writes with his new _____.
- ○ pet
- ○ pen
- ○ peg

6 He will draw a _____ with it.
- ○ map
- ○ man
- ○ mat

7 After school, Ben plays with his _____.
- ○ car
- ○ cat
- ○ cap

8 At eight o'clock he goes to _____.
- ○ beg
- ○ bet
- ○ bed

THINK! How is your school day like Ben's?

10 Lesson 3
Final consonants

 Ask your child to think of words ending with the letters *t, k, p, x,* and *l.*

CONTENTS

Consonants, Hard and Soft c and g

UNIT 1

Theme: Celebrations

Short and Long Vowels

UNIT 2

Theme: Home Sweet Home

Compounds, Blends and Digraphs, Y as a Consonant and a Vowel, R-Controlled Vowels

UNIT 3

Theme: What an Imagination!

Contractions, Plurals, Suffixes

UNIT 4

Theme: A Working World

Vowel Pairs, Digraphs, Diphthongs

UNIT 5

Theme: By the Sea

Prefixes, Base Words, Suffixes, Syllables

UNIT 6

Theme: Taking Care of Our Earth

Synonyms, Antonyms, Homonyms, Dictionary Skills

UNIT 7

Theme: Express Yourself!

Name _____

▶ Say each word in the box below. Write the words that contain a hard **c** sound under the picture of the cap. Write the words that contain a soft **c** sound under the picture of the cereal.

When the letter **c** is followed by the vowels **a, o,** or **u,** it has a hard sound. Hard **c** has a **k** sound. When **c** is followed by **e, i,** or **y,** it usually has a soft sound. Soft **c** has an **s** sound.

cat	**c**ot	**c**ut
la**c**e	**c**ity	fan**c**y

actor	carriage	cinema	cub	doctor	pencil
candy	celery	coat	cymbal	grocery	price
cattle	cellar	corn	decide	palace	recess
		cow	decorate		

► **Say the words in each box. Draw a line to connect the words that have the same g sound.**

1		2	
page	game	figure	large
flag	engine	gold	giraffe

3		4	
orange	gym	gutter	ago
sugar	organ	pigeon	arrange

► **Write the words from above in the correct columns.**

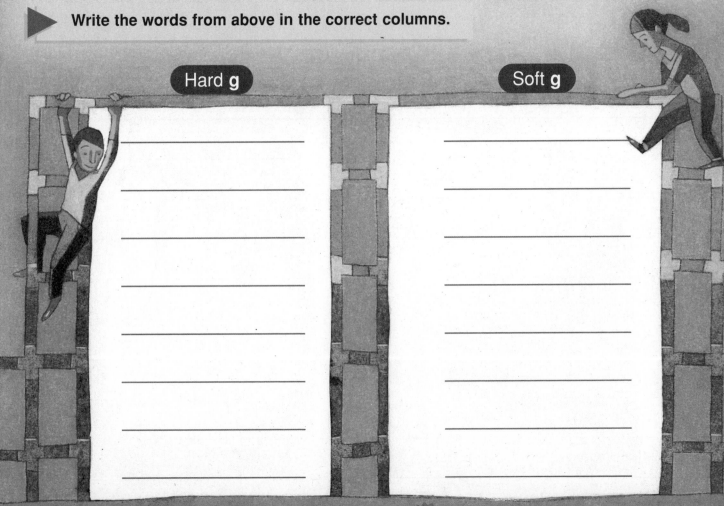

Hard **g**

Soft **g**

Lesson 4
Hard and soft g

Home

Ask your child to use the words on this page in sentences.

Name _____

Circle each word that has the soft c sound or the soft g sound.

> **RULE**
> When the letter **c** or **g** is followed by **e, i,** or **y**, the **c** or **g** usually has a soft sound.
>
> ra**ce**   pa**ge**

ice	can	lace	came	fancy	gym
gate	giant	rice	large	huge	wig
rage	center	celery	because	coyote	general
hug	city	judge	page	face	cookies
game	engine	dance	leg	ceiling	police
fence	garden	carriage	guess	magic	place
tag	nice	bridge	giraffe	gem	cover

Circle each word that has the hard sound of c or g.

1. Everyone had a good time at Carol's birthday party.

2. The guests came dressed in fancy costumes.

3. Lance was a detective who solved strange crimes.

4. Janice wore a colorful gown and an orange wig.

5. A magician did tricks and juggled cans.

6. The children played bingo and had sack races.

7. Then Carol's mother gave them cake and ice cream.

8. Carol gasped as she opened her cards and presents.

9. Curtis gave her a goldfish in a bowl.

10. Gary the cat stared at it curiously.

11. He thought he could catch it for dinner.

12. The children giggled when Gary was carried outside.

 Why do you think everyone had a good time at the party?

Lesson 5
Hard and soft c and g
13

Read the words. Write the word that matches the clue.

call	face	gym	judge
card	game	hug	race
center	gift	huge	tag

1. a present   __ [□] __ __

2. a sport or contest   __ __ __ __

3. a running contest   __ __ [□] __

4. part of the head   __ __ __ [□]

5. a label or ticket   __ __ __

6. to say in a loud way   [□] __ __ __

7. the middle   __ __ __ __ __ [□]

8. a person who decides   __ __ __ __ [□] __

9. it comes in the mail   __ [□] __ __

10. to put your arms around   __ __ __

11. a place to play a game   __ __ [□]

12. very, very big   __ __ __ __

Write the letters from the boxes to find out what the
award winners ate.   __ __ __ __ __ __ __ __

Lesson 5
Hard and soft c and g

Home

Name _____

Phonics & Spelling

▶ Read the words. Write each word under the heading where it belongs.

Word List	candy	cement	corn	game
	guess	gym	page	price

Soft c	Soft g	Hard c	Hard g
1. _____	2. _____	3. _____	4. _____
5. _____	6. _____	7. _____	8. _____

▶ Read the words. Write each word under the heading where it belongs.

Word List	balloon	cement	dragon	leaf	lizard
	ruler	seven	window	zipper	radio

Consonant in the Middle

9. _____   10. _____   11. _____

12. _____   13. _____   14. _____

15. _____   16. _____   17. _____

Consonant at the End

18. _____   19. _____   20. _____

21. _____   22. _____   23. _____

24. _____   25. _____   26. _____

Phonics & Writing

▶ Write an entry in your journal telling why you would like a special person to visit you. Use some of these words in your writing.

balloon	games	page	seven
candy	gym	price	visit
corn	magic	ruler	zipper

_____

_____

_____

_____

_____

_____

_____

_____

Book Corner

Obon
by Ruth Suyenaga
Illustrated by Yoshi Miyake

A young girl discovers her heritage during the celebration of the Japanese festival of Obon.

Home

Ask your child to read his or her journal entry to you.

Author! Author!

WELCOME

1

Mrs. Winter's class was very excited. A special guest was coming to visit. He was Cyrus Singer, a children's book author. This was a real celebration!

FOLD

FOLD

Near the end of class, the students had a surprise for Mr. Singer. "We've already read one of your books," they said. They acted out the story as a play. Mr. Singer was very pleased!

Whom would you invite to an author celebration? Explain why you chose this author.

TALK ABOUT IT

4

WELCOME CYRUS SINGER

When Mr. Singer entered the room, everyone was quiet. Mrs. Winter said, "Welcome to our class, Mr. Singer."

Then he set down a pile of books that he had written. Mr. Singer spoke about being an author. He told about how he got ideas for his stories. He said, "They're often based on people I know. Sometimes they're about things that really happened to me."

2

After he finished his talk, the author asked, "Does anyone have a question?" Many students raised their hands. They wanted to know what he did to become a really good author. Mr. Singer smiled. He explained that good authors work very hard. He said, "I change a story until it sounds just right. But writing is also fun!"

3

Name _____

Read the words in the box. Write each word from the box in the columns that describe the position of its consonants.

vat	gas	soap	pedal	leaf	hurry
wagon	zoo	cab	yellow	jiffy	dog
hated	funny	happy	room	music	comic
near	cowboy	jazz	tow	bike	hazy

	Beginning Consonant	**Middle Consonant**	**Ending Consonant**
p	1. _____	13. _____	25. _____
d	2. _____	14. _____	26. _____
b	3. _____	15. _____	27. _____
l	4. _____	16. _____	28. _____
m	5. _____	17. _____	29. _____
s	6. _____	18. _____	30. _____
r	7. _____	19. _____	31. _____
n	8. _____	20. _____	32. _____
g	9. _____	21. _____	33. _____
t	10. _____	22. _____	34. _____
z	11. _____	23. _____	35. _____
f	12. _____	24. _____	36. _____

Fill in the circle beside the word that belongs in each sentence.

1. Alice ____ a package in the mail.   ○ got   ○ gym

2. She was ____ that it was from Carl.   ○ curtain   ○ certain

3. The package was ___!   ○ huge   ○ hug

4. Alice tried to ____ what was in it.   ○ gem   ○ guess

5. She ____ opened the box.   ○ cement   ○ carefully

6. A ____ red kite was inside.   ○ giant   ○ garden

7. "I ____ believe my eyes," said Alice.   ○ cent   ○ can't

8. "I'll ____ Carl right away to thank him."   ○ call   ○ cell

Write the word choices listed above in the correct columns.

9	Hard **c**	10	Soft **c**
_____		_____	
_____		_____	
_____		_____	
_____		_____	

11	Hard **g**	12	Soft **g**
_____		_____	
_____		_____	
_____		_____	
_____		_____	

Lesson 8
Hard and soft c, g: Checkup

▶ **Find the hidden pictures.**

 What do you like to do on a sunny day?

Home Letter

Dear Family,

In this unit, your child will be learning about different kinds of homes. He or she will also be learning about words with short and long vowel sounds like these example words.

Short
hat | bed | dish | top | rug

Long
tape | seal | kite | cone | tube

At-Home Activities

Here are two activities that you and your child might like to do together.

▶ With your child, make a list of pictures that are hidden on page 21. Then ask your child to make a list of the short vowel words and long vowel words.

▶ Ask your child to draw a map of your neighborhood, showing where friends or relatives live.

Book Corner

To extend the unit theme, you may wish to read these books with your child.

The Floating House
by Scott R. Sanders

In 1815 a flatboat carries the McClure family down the Ohio River to their new home.

Big Meeting
by Dee Parmer Woodtor

Celebrate home and family in this charming book about an annual family reunion.

Sincerely,

Name _____

 Say the name of each picture. Color each picture whose name has the short sound of **a**.

1	2	3	4
5	6	7	8
9	10	11	12

 Circle the words with a short **a** in the puzzle. Use the words in the box to help you.

```
B    A    T    C    F
H    R    Q    A    A
A    X    R    T    N
N    H    A    T    W
D    C    A    K    E
G    L    A    S    S
```

ax	glass
bat	hand
cat	hat
fan	cake

Lesson 9
Short vowel a

23

Read each sentence. Circle the words with the short a sound and write them on the lines. Then draw a picture to show what the sentence tells about.

1 Ann had fun at the beach.

_____

_____

_____

2 She ran with her friends Vicky
and Jack.

_____

_____

_____

3 Dad helped them make two
sand castles.

_____

_____

_____

4 Then they swam fast to the raft.

_____

_____

_____

5 They napped in the van on the ride
back home.

_____

_____

_____

THINK! What else do you think they can do at the beach?

24
Lesson 9
Short vowel a words

Home Ask your child to think of rhyming
words for each short *a* word.

Name _____

1	2	3	4
_____	_____	_____	_____

5	6	7	8
_____	_____	_____	_____

 Say each word in the first column. Find a word in the second column that rhymes with it. Draw a line to connect the two words.

9		10			11		
kick	fig	hip		tin	wig		hit
rip	hill	pin		big	lit		rig
dig	sick	pig		sip	dip		bin
bill	lip	did		lid	tin		tip

Lesson 10
Short vowel i

25

Say the words in the box below. Write the words with a short a sound under the picture of the cat. Write the words with a short i sound under the picture of the fish.

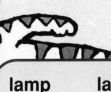

lamp	late	Jim	gift	if	back
bike	cake	cat	ham	died	zip
hit	map	rain	an	sip	tick
ask	dime	fish	milk	ran	at
pin	dish	wax	will	rap	flat

Short **a**

Short **i**

_____   _____

_____   _____

_____   _____

_____   _____

_____   _____

Home

Ask your child to name the cat and fish using short *a* and short *i* words.

Name _____

> **Write the name of each picture. Then circle the vowel in each word.**

1 _____	**2** _____	**3** _____	**4** _____
5 _____	**6** _____	**7** _____	**8** _____

> **Fill in the circle beside the word that belongs in each sentence. Write the word on the line.**

○ Gas
○ Gus
9. _____ is a very large duck.   ○ Got

○ sick
○ sun
10. He likes to sleep in the _____.   ○ sad

○ tan
○ tub
11. One day he tried to swim in a _____.   ○ tent

○ stick
○ stuck
12. It was too small so he got _____.   ○ stack

○ luck
○ lick
13. What bad _____ for a very large duck!   ○ lock

Say each word. Change the short u to short a. Write the new word in the first column. Then change the short a to short i. Write the new word in the second column.

	Short a word	**Short i word**
1. fun	fan	fin
2. us		
3. bug		
4. hum		
5. hut		
6. but		
7. luck		
8. tuck		
9. bun		
10. lump		
11. sung		
12. rug		
13. must		
14. stuck		
15. truck		
16. sunk		

Ask your child for a rhyming word for each group of words.

Name _____

1	2	3	4

_____	_____	_____	_____

5	6	7	8
_____	_____	_____	_____

▶ **Read the paragraph. Underline the words with the short o sound.
Then write those words on the lines.**

A Summer Picnic

Last summer the Todd family went on a picnic. It was a warm day, but not too hot. They had a pot of beans, hamburgers, and juice. After lunch Dot and Tom helped Mom find some shiny rocks. They put them into the bottom of a box. Bobby, the baby, went with Dad to watch the ducks by the pond. They saw a little toad hop in the grass. The family had a lot of fun that day.

9. _____   10. _____   11. _____

12. _____   13. _____   14. _____

15. _____   16. _____   17. _____

18. _____   19. _____   20. _____

21. _____   22. _____   23. _____

1. cat _____ _____
2. bad _____ _____
3. tip _____ _____
4. lock _____ _____
5. on _____ _____
6. big _____ _____
7. ham _____ _____
8. fun _____ _____

► **Find the word in the cat that will finish each sentence.**
Write the word on the line.

9. I love my tabby _____, Max.

10. He sleeps _____ the rug in my room.

11. Sometimes Max plays with a _____.

12. He likes to _____ in and out of it.

13. I gave _____ some string to play with, too.

14. It was _____ to see Max try to catch it.

15. Once he was very _____.

16. Max jumped on _____ of the counter.

17. He made some milk _____ over.

18. I was going to _____ the floor.

19. Then Max started to _____ up the milk.

20. He cleaned the mess _____ a hurry!

bad	lick
bag	mop
cat	on
fun	run
him	tip
in	top

THINK! Why might Max be a good pet?

Home Ask your child to write a story using the words from the cat.

Name _____

1	2	3	4

 Circle the name of each picture.

5

nuts
sent
nest
test

6

test
tent
ten
net

7

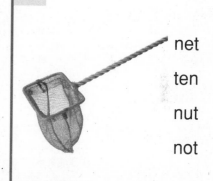

net
ten
nut
not

8

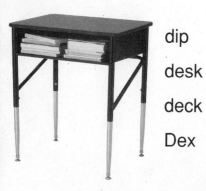

dip
desk
deck
Dex

9

let
pat
get
jet

10

ship
shell
bell
shall

Read the words in the box. Write the words with the same short vowel sound in the correct window. Then write your own word with the same vowel sound on the last line.

top	fit	bus	cab	cup
jet	pen	pig	rock	wig
tub	box	tag	step	map

a   e   i

o   u

Lesson 13
Review short vowels a, e, i, o, u

 Home

Have your child put the words on the roof in alphabetical order.

Name _____

A HOUSE FOR REX

Meg was opening birthday presents when the doorbell rang. She opened the door and saw a box. The box had holes in it and made a thumping sound.

"What could it be?" thought Meg as she opened the box. It was a puppy!

"I'll call you Rex," Meg said as she ran into the house to show Mom, Dad, and her brother Tim.

Soon, Mom said that Rex was too big to stay in the house. So Meg and Tim decided to build a doghouse. They found wood, nails, and red paint in the garage. Dad helped Tim and Meg build the doghouse, but Meg got to paint it by herself. Finally, the doghouse was done. Rex was so happy that he knocked over the can of paint.

"Maybe I'll call you Red now instead of Rex!" said Meg.

1. Meg named her new pet _____.

2. He arrived in a _____ on Meg's front step.

3. Mom said that Rex was too _____ to stay in the house.

4. Meg and _____ decided to build a doghouse.

5. The doghouse is painted _____.

6. Rex knocked over the _____ of paint.

Phonics & Writing

What if Rex didn't like his doghouse after all? Write an ad to sell Rex's doghouse. Remember to use some of the words in the box and your own words.

ball	bell	blob	bus	can	day	dish
hop	jump	lock	pond	red	sun	tap

Lesson 14
Review short vowels: Writing

Ask your child to read his or her ad to sell the doghouse.

Name ______________________________

RULE

If a one-syllable word has two vowels, the first vowel usually stands for the long sound, and the second vowel is silent. If the first vowel is **i**, the word has the long **i** sound.

b**i**k**e** d**i**m**e** p**ie**

Circle the word that names each picture.

1
kit
kite

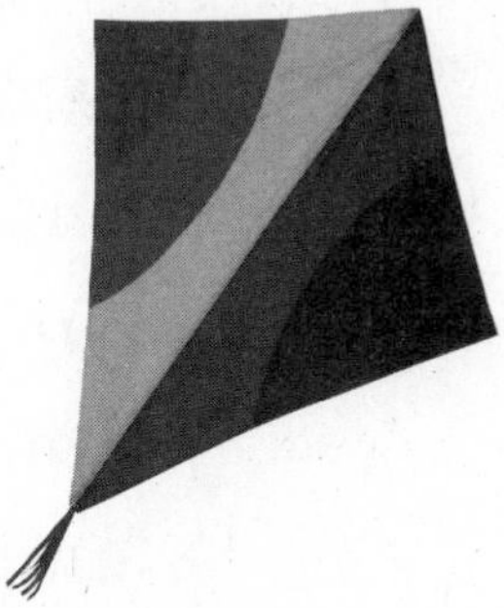

2
ride
rid

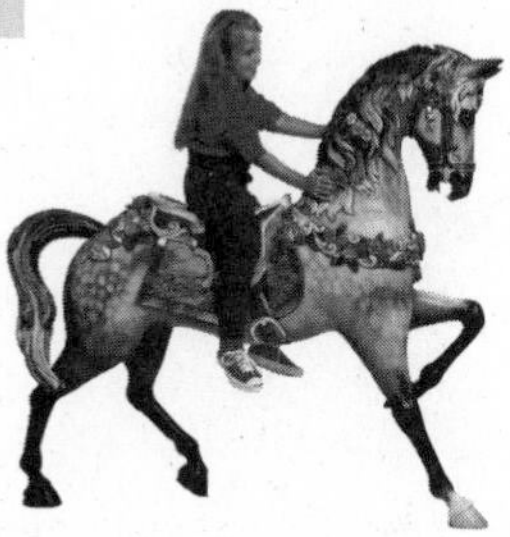

3
pine
pin

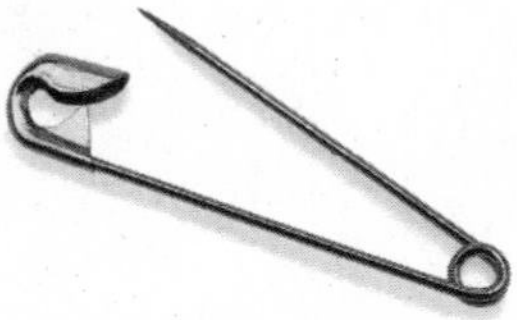

4
rip
ripe

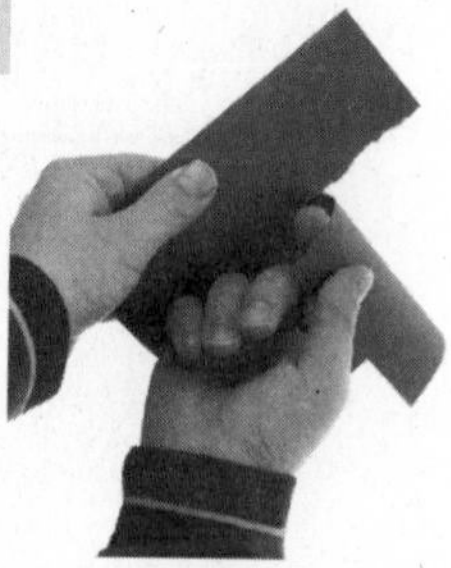

5
bit
bite

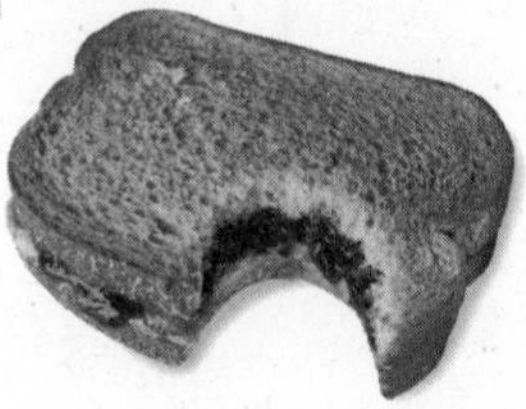

6
fir
fire

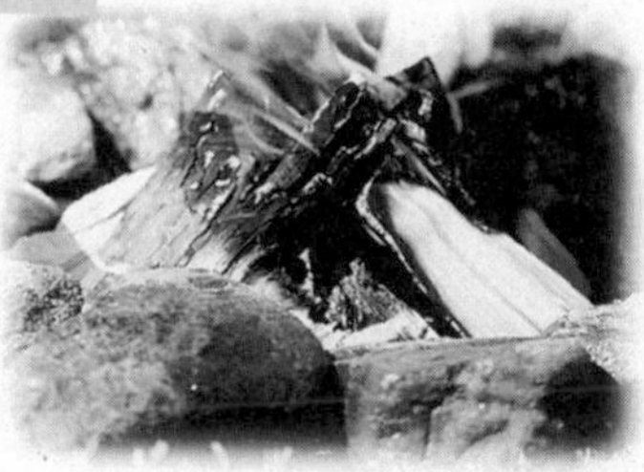

7
Tim
time

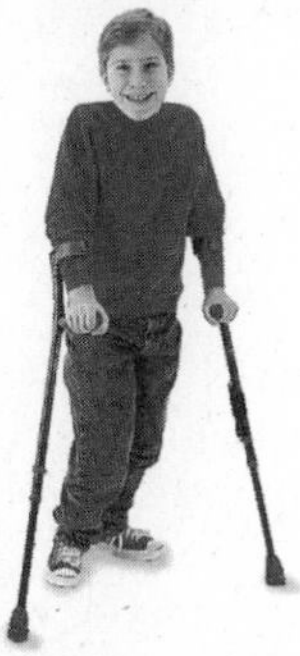

8
pile
pit

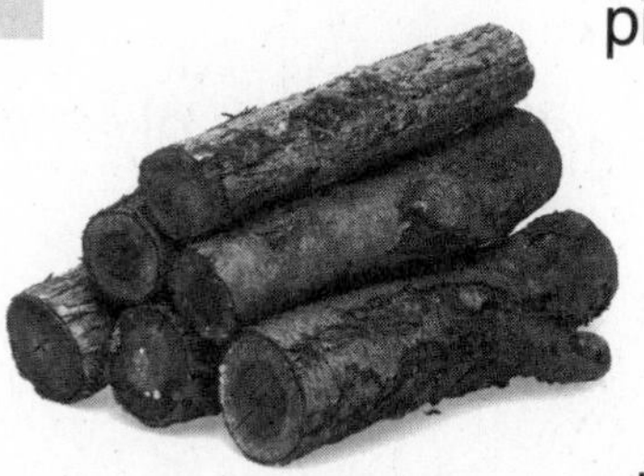

9

dime
dim

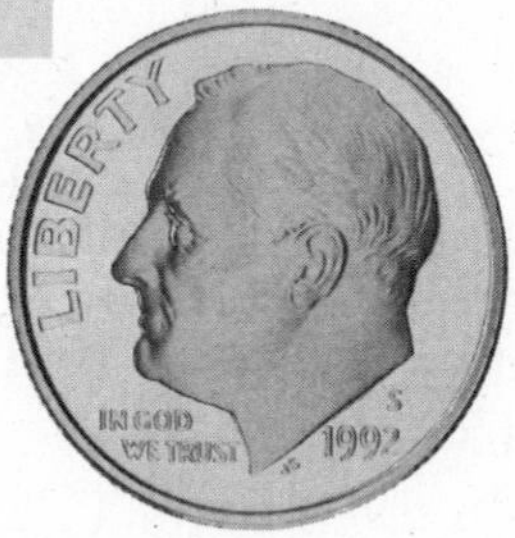

10
sit
site

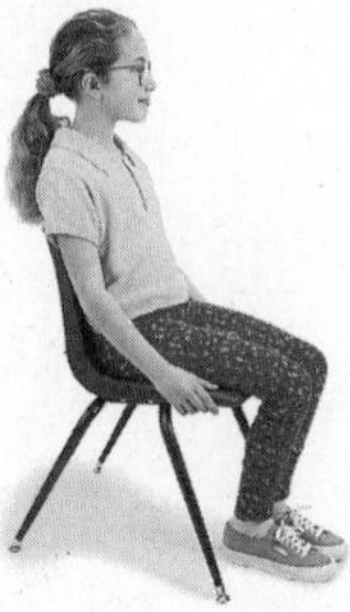

11
fine
fin

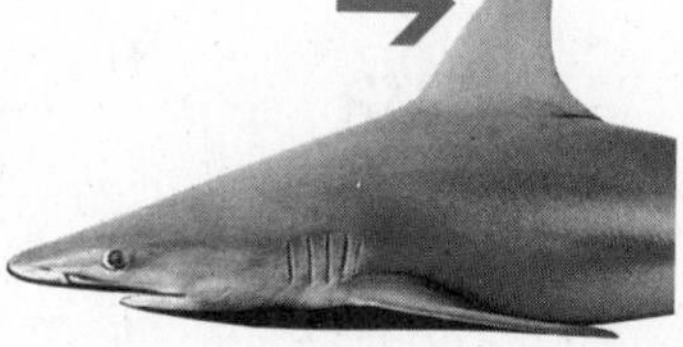

12
slide
slid

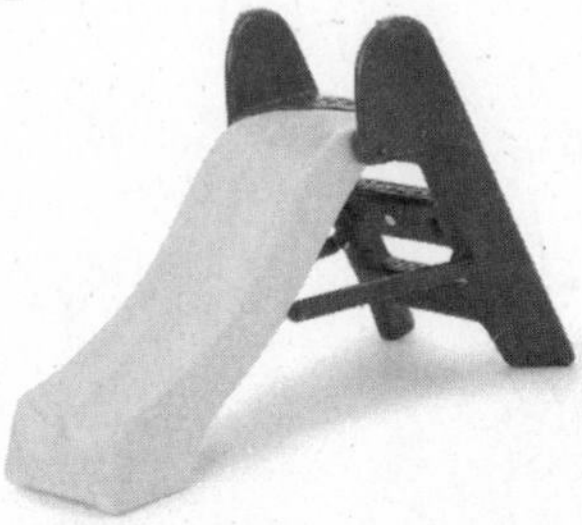

Find the word in the box that will finish each sentence. Write the word on the line.

away
came
day
face
five
kite
mail
rain
smiled
stripes
tail
tie

1. Kay got a new _____ to fly.

2. It came in the _____ from Mike.

3. A grin lit up Kay's _____.

4. The kite had blue and red _____.

5. It had _____ yellow stars.

6. It also had a long _____.

7. Kay had to _____ a string on it.

8. She flew it on a very windy _____.

9. When the wind stopped, the kite _____ down.

10. Then it began to _____, and Kate ran home.

11. She carefully put the kite _____.

12. Kay _____ as she thought of flying it again.

Circle each word that has a long vowel sound.

13. whale	pie	pail	big	pig	fine
14. jam	blame	nine	bike	dime	gas
15. hit	save	fist	pipe	trip	man
16. sand	mice	plate	fish	cat	trash
17. ate	name	dish	five	game	snap
18. ran	hand	map	rain	pain	line

38

Lesson 16
Long vowel i

Home · Ask your child to say and spell the words in the box with the long a sound.

Name _____

RULE

If one syllable has two vowels, the first vowel usually stands for the long sound, and the second vowel is silent. If the first vowel is **u**, the word has the long **u** sound.

t**u**be   gl**u**e   fr**u**it

1

flunk

flute

Luke will play his _____ in a concert.

2

sun

Sue

He will play a song with _____.

3

tune

ton

They will play a popular _____.

4

sit

suit

Luke's mom will buy him a new

_____.

5

cut

cute

Then Luke will get a

hair _____.

6

hug

huge

After the recital, Dad will give him

a _____.

7

fun

fruit

Then Luke will have _____ juice and cookies.

 THINK! How will Luke feel after the concert is over?

> Say each word in the box and listen for the long vowel sounds.
> Write the words in the correct column.

tune	dime	stay	ride	mule	fine
lake	pail	use	tape	lie	came
pie	suit	tuba	like	cube	rain

Long a	Long i	Long u
1. cane	8. bike	15. tube
2. _____	9. _____	16. _____
3. _____	10. _____	17. _____
4. _____	11. _____	18. _____
5. _____	12. _____	19. _____
6. _____	13. _____	20. _____
7. _____	14. _____	21. _____

> Say each word. Write two words that rhyme with it.

lake	like	suit
22. _____	24. _____	26. _____
23. _____	25. _____	27. _____

Lesson 17
Review long vowels a, i, u

Home

Ask your child to add rhyming words to the lists above.

Name _____

RULE

If one syllable has two vowels, the first vowel usually stands for the long sound, and the second vowel is silent. If the first vowel is **o**, the word has the long **o** sound.

b**o**n**e**   g**oa**t   t**oe**

► **Circle the name of each picture.**

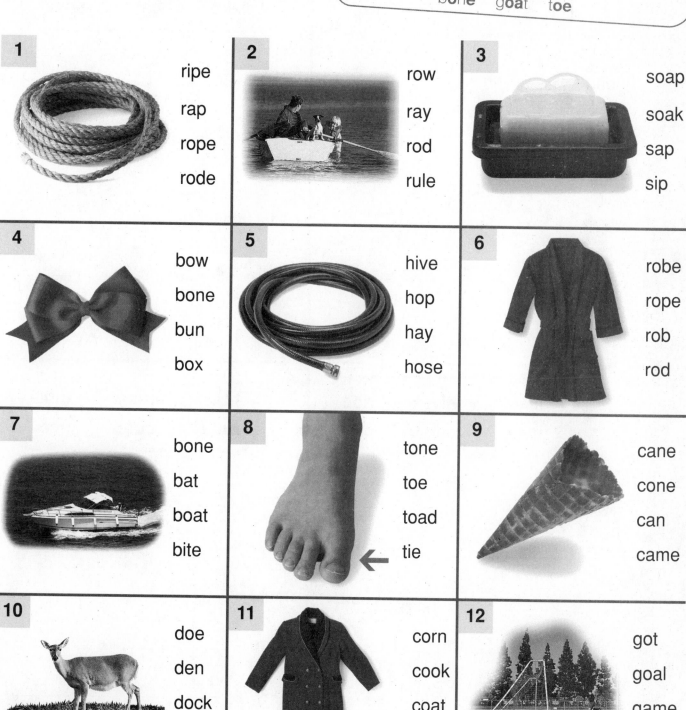

1
ripe
rap
rope
rode

2
row
ray
rod
rule

3
soap
soak
sap
sip

4
bow
bone
bun
box

5
hive
hop
hay
hose

6
robe
rope
rob
rod

7
bone
bat
boat
bite

8
tone
toe
toad
tie

9
cane
cone
can
came

10
doe
den
dock
duck

11
corn
cook
coat
cube

12
got
goal
game
gas

Say each word. Find the word in the box that rhymes with it, and write the word on the line.

1

cone	coat	row
rode	hope	pole

load _____

boat _____

hoe _____

bone _____

soap _____

hole _____

2

pail	late	made
lake	way	save

wait _____

day _____

sale _____

cake _____

paid _____

wave _____

3

like	hive	ride
mine	bite	pie

dive _____

lie _____

line _____

bike _____

tied _____

kite _____

4

tune	tube	mule
rude	cute	use

June _____

rule _____

mute _____

cube _____

fuse _____

dude _____

Lesson 18
Review long vowels a, i, u, o

Home

Ask your child to draw a line between the words that rhyme on page 41.

Name _____

Look at the picture. Circle the word that names the picture. Then complete the sentence by writing the word on the line.

#			
1		Pet Pete	_____ likes to visit the zoo.
2		seals sells	He thinks the _____ are funny.
3		set seat	Pete finds a _____ to watch them play.
4		tent teeth	He likes the lion with its big _____.
5		meat met	The lion likes to eat _____.
6		eagle enter	Pete's favorite animal is the _____.
7		trend tree	It sits up high in a _____.
8	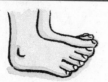	fell feet	Pete's _____ hurt at the end of the day.

THINK! What animals do you like to see at the zoo?

Lesson 19
Long vowel e: Words in context

43

Say the name of each picture. Color the animals whose names contain the long vowel sound shown in the box.

1

Long a

jay   snail   cat   whale

2

Long i

tiger   mice   kitten   pig

3

Long u

skunk   mule   duck   puppy

4

Long o

fox   goat   doe   ox

5

Long e

seal   hen   bee   eagle

Lesson 19
Review long vowels a, e, i, o, u

 Ask your child to name two other words for each long vowel sound.

Name _____

 **Phonics & Spelling**

▶ Use the clues to write the words in each puzzle.

Word List

bell	day	hand	luck	ride	
boat	flute	kick	pile	tape	team
cone	gift	lock	pond	tent	

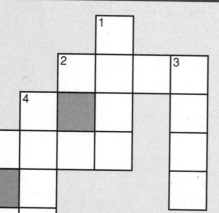

Across

2. ring the ____
5. wrap a ____
7. ____ the door
8. wave your ____

Down

1. sleep in a ____
3. good ____
4. ____ the ball
6. fish _____

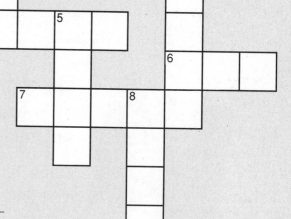

Across

2. ice-cream ____
4. cut the ____
6. a sunny ____
7. play the ____

Down

1. row the ____
3. ____ the bus
5. put papers in a ____
8. ____ players

Lesson 20
Review short and long vowels: Spelling

45

Phonics & Writing

Write a postcard to a friend describing your home. Use the words in the box and your own words.

bell	day	hand	luck	pond	tape
boat	flute	kick	meat	ride	tent
cone	gift	lock	pile	sail	team

_____

_____

_____

_____

_____

_____

_____

_____

Book Corner

The Thirty-six Cats of Marie Tatin
by Sylvie Chausse
illustrated by François Crozat

Marie Tatin has a lovely home but nobody to share it with until a friend gives her some interesting advice.

Ask your child to draw a picture of your home for display.

Animal HOMES

Animals live in many different kinds of homes. Some small animals, like chipmunks, dig burrows and live there for a long time. Some larger animals, like bears and wolves, live in dens. Dens can be in the ground, in caves, in thick bushes, or behind rocks.

FOLD

FOLD

Some insects, like these African termites, build nests of mud called termite mounds. The mud is baked by the hot desert sun until it is as hard as concrete! Mounds like this one can be 20 feet tall and are used for many years. The mounds are crisscrossed with tunnels that lead to nurseries and food supplies.

TALK ABOUT IT

Why do you think there are so many different kinds of animal homes?

Lesson 21
Review short and long vowels: Take-Home Book

47

Ospreys, a kind of hawk, build their homes on the top of tall telephone poles or dead trees. They often use their very large nests of twigs and sticks year after year. In fact, some ospreys have been known to use the same nest for 40 years in a row!

FOLD FOLD

Some reptiles that live in hot and dry places, like iguanas and snakes, may live under rocks. Rocks protect them from the hot sun during days that can reach 120 degrees! Other reptiles that live in colder, wetter places make their homes under piles of leaves. Did you know that some snakes even live in trees?

Lesson 21
Review short and long vowels: Take-Home Book

The Spangled Pandemonium

The Spangled Pandemonium
Is missing from the zoo.
He bent the bars the barest bit,
And slithered glibly through.

He crawled across the moated wall,
He climbed the mango tree,
And when his keeper scrambled up,
He nipped him in the knee.

To all of you a warning
Not to wander after dark,
Or if you must, make very sure
You stay out of the park.

For the Spangled Pandemonium
Is missing from the zoo,
And since he nipped his keeper,
He would just as soon nip you.

Palmer Brown

▶ **Read the poem aloud to enjoy the rhyme and rhythm.**

THINK! Would you see a Spangled Pandemonium at the zoo? Why or why not?

Home Letter

Dear Family,

In this unit, your child will be learning compound words (sunshine and basketball); syllables in words, such as pen/cil; y as a consonant and as a vowel (why and carry); consonant blends and digraphs (blanket and echo); and r-controlled vowels (garden and tiger).

We will also be talking about imaginative things, as the poem on page 51 illustrates. To reinforce the unit skills and theme, you may wish to do the following activities with your child.

At-Home Activities

▶ Read with your child the poem "The Spangled Pandemonium" on page 51. Then ask your child to find all the words in the poem that begin with two consonants, such as climbed, spangled, and crawled.

▶ Watch a humor-based television show or video with your child. Then discuss why he or she laughed at certain parts and not others.

Book Corner

You and your child might enjoy reading these books together. Look for them in your local library.

Wallpaper from Space
by Daniel Pinkwater

In this humorous story, Steve retreats from house redecorating by traveling inside the new wallpaper in his room.

Nonsense Songs
by Edward Lear

A delightful collection of Lear's nonsense songs and poetry.

Sincerely,

Name _____

Say each word. Write the two words that make up the compound word on the lines.

A **compound word** is made up of two or more words joined together to make a new word. **Homework** is **work** you do at **home.**

1. teapot _____ _____

2. sunshine _____ _____

3. seagull _____ _____

4. beehive _____ _____

5. beanbag _____ _____

6. pancake _____ _____

7. wayside _____ _____

8. airway _____ _____

9. necktie _____ _____

10. milkweed _____ _____

11. peanuts _____ _____

12. treetop _____ _____

13. waterfall _____ _____

14. overcoat _____ _____

backpack	backyard	bathtub	countertop	dustpan	fireplace
outside	overhead	paintbrush	playmate	postcard	raincoat
rattlesnake	sailboat	seashell	snowflake	treehouse	treetop
waterfall	weekend				

1. a brush for painting _____

2. the top of a tree _____

3. opposite of inside _____

4. a coat worn in rain _____

5. a pan to scoop dust _____

6. a card that is mailed _____

7. a shell near the sea _____

8. a flake of snow _____

9. a place for a fire _____

10. a tub for bathing _____

11. the end of the week _____

12. a snake that rattles _____

13. someone to play with _____

14. the top of the counter _____

15. a bag to carry on the back _____

16. the back of the yard _____

17. over your head _____

18. a boat that sails _____

19. water that falls _____

20. a house in a tree _____

Name _____

Say the name of each picture. In the box below it, write the number of syllables you hear in the picture name.

1

2

3

4

5

6

7

8

9

10

11

12

13

14

15

16

Look at each word. Write the number of vowels you **see** in the first column. Say the word. Write the number of vowels you **hear** in the second column.

HINT

If you hear one vowel sound, the word has one syllable. If you hear two vowel sounds, the word has two syllables.

pen   pencil

Vowels

	See	Hear
1. pencil	____	____
2. jeep	____	____
3. milk	____	____
4. rabbit	____	____
5. basement	____	____
6. music	____	____
7. beans	____	____
8. hillside	____	____
9. mailbox	____	____
10. peanuts	____	____
11. picnic	____	____
12. ate	____	____
13. sidetrack	____	____
14. pail	____	____
15. tune	____	____

Vowels

	See	Hear
16. basket	____	____
17. wagon	____	____
18. mitten	____	____
19. pancake	____	____
20. visit	____	____
21. kit	____	____
22. cannot	____	____
23. cabin	____	____
24. sailboat	____	____
25. race	____	____
26. Pete	____	____
27. pie	____	____
28. beanbag	____	____
29. treetop	____	____
30. rode	____	____

Home   Ask your child to tell you a story using six words on this page.

Name _____

Remember that in a **consonant blend** the sounds of the consonants blend together, but each sound is heard. Listen for the **l** blends in the following words.

black **pl**ant

Write the name of each picture. Circle the **l** blend that stands for the beginning sound in its name.

1	2	3
_____	_____	_____
4 	5	6 
_____	_____	_____
7 	8 	9
_____	_____	_____
10 	11 	12
_____	_____	_____
13 	14	15
_____	_____	_____

For each word, find two words in the clock with the same l blend. Write them on the lines.

1. clock _____ _____

2. black _____ _____

3. flat _____ _____

4. glad _____ _____

5. plant _____ _____

6. sled _____ _____

block	glow
flag	blue
sleep	play
clean	please
slide	glue
fly	clip

Read each sentence carefully. Find the word in the glass that will complete the sentence. Write the word on the line.

7. As Flora left school, the wind was _____

8. There were many _____ in the sky.

9. It was too cold to stop to _____ .

10. Flora _____ her hands in her pockets.

11. She had left her _____ at home.

12. Flora quickly walked the six _____ home.

13. When she got there, she was _____ .

14. Her mom gave her a _____ of warm milk.

15. Then Flora sat _____ to the fire.

blocks
blowing
close
clouds
glad
glass
gloves
play
slipped

Name _____

► **Write the name of each picture. Circle the s blend that stands for the beginning sound in its name.**

RULE

Remember that in a **consonant blend** the sounds of the consonants blend together, but each sound is heard. Listen for the **s** blends in the following words.

skid   **sp**ell

1 	2 	3
4 	5	6 
7 	8 	9 
10 	11 	12 
13 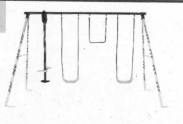	14 	15 

1. Our first camping trip was (special, slender). _____

2. We (stamp, spent) five days in the mountains. _____

3. Our trip was in early (string, spring). _____

4. The weather was (still, spill) quite chilly. _____

5. We wore (scatters, sweaters) under our coats. _____

6. We also wore two pairs of (stockings, snails). _____

7. I tripped on a (stump, sport) while hiking. _____

8. My ankle became very (swollen, squirrel). _____

9. We all (swept, screamed) when we saw a snake. _____

10. The snake just (splashed, slithered) away. _____

Read each word. Circle the **s** blend that is used in the word. Write the word on the line.

11. skid _____ 12. stamp _____

13. smile _____ 14. spray _____

15. scale _____ 16. stream _____

17. sniff _____ 18. spell _____

19. sweep _____ 20. scrub _____

21. smell _____ 22. snow _____

Home

Ask your child to tell you a story using s blend words not on this page.

Sometimes consonant blends can be at the end of a word. Say the name of each picture. Circle the word that names the picture.

1
stamp   stand

2
mast   mask

3
trunk   trust

4
limp   list

5
kind   king

6
raft   ramp

7
hang   hand

8
sprint   spring

9
plank   plant

10
wing   wink

11
milk   mint

12
pomp   pond

13
desk   dent

14
sing   sink

15
gill   gift

16
shelf   send

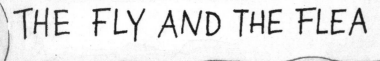

THE FLY AND THE FLEA

A fly and a flea flew up in a flue.
Said the fly to the flea, "What shall we do?"
"Let's fly," said the flea.
"Let's flee," said the fly.
So they fluttered and flew up the flue.

1. _____   2. _____   3. _____

4. _____   5. _____   6. _____

Write your own nonsense poem. Choose words from the box
or your own words with the same beginning or ending
consonant blend. Write the words on the lines.

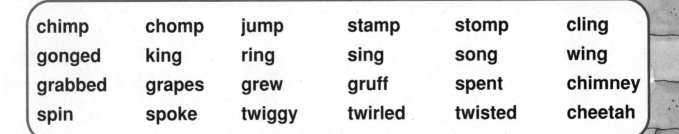

chimp	chomp	jump	stamp	stomp	cling
gonged	king	ring	sing	song	wing
grabbed	grapes	grew	gruff	spent	chimney
spin	spoke	twiggy	twirled	twisted	cheetah

7. A _____ and a _____ _____ in a _____

8. Said the _____ to the _____, "What shall we do?"

9. "Let's _____," said the _____ to the _____.

10. "Let's _____," said the _____ to the _____.

11. So they _____ and _____ up the _____.

Ask your child to read his or her poem
to you.

Name _____

► **Add y to each blend to make a word. Write the word on the line.**

1. fr _____   2. cr _____

3. tr _____   4. dr _____

5. sk _____   6. sl _____

7. fl _____   8. spr _____

► **Read each question. Use one or more of the words you just made to answer it. Write your answer on the lines. Use a complete sentence.**

9. Where do you look to see clouds?

_____

_____

10. Why do we use umbrellas when it rains?

_____

_____

11. What can an airplane do in the sky?

_____

_____

12. What sometimes happens if you fall and hurt yourself?

_____

_____

Say each word in the box and listen for the **y** sound. Write the words in the correct column.

RULE

When **y** is the only vowel at the end of a syllable, or a word of one syllable, **y** has the long **i** sound. When **y** is the only vowel at the end of a word of more than one syllable, **y** usually has the long **e** sound.

fl**y**   cr**y**ing   prett**y**

bunny	cry
every	grocery
muddy	shy
sky	swiftly
trying	why

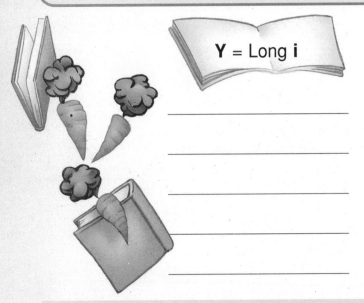

Y = Long i

Y = Long e

_____   _____

_____   _____

_____   _____

_____   _____

Find the word in the box that will complete each sentence. Write the word on the line.

1. My _____ likes to do things together.

2. Sometimes we go to the _____.

3. There are so _____ books to choose from.

4. Dad likes _____ books about ancient Egypt.

5. I like books with lots of _____ jokes.

6. Mom likes books with _____ flowers in them.

7. Once we checked out more than _____ books.

8. It was difficult to _____ them!

carry

family

funny

history

library

many

pretty

twenty

Lesson 29
Y as a vowel

Home

Ask your child to describe an activity that your family likes to do together.

Name _____

Say the name of each picture. Find the name in the box. Write it on the line.

| baby | bunny | city | cry | fly | party |
| penny | pony | pretty | puppy | sky | try |

1
_____

2
_____

3
_____

4
_____

5
_____

6
_____

7
_____

8
_____

Say the first word in each row. Circle the words that have the same **y** sound as that word.

RULE

When **y** comes at the beginning of a word, **y** is a consonant.

yolk

9	**yes**	sky	yard	yellow	windy
10	**many**	pretty	yet	dry	sweetly
11	**fly**	lovely	yell	try	why
12	**happy**	sorry	every	yard	fry
13	**year**	many	yolk	funny	yarn

Lesson 30   67
Y as a vowel and as a consonant

The Ice-Cream Man

One afternoon my brother Craig and I saw a jet go over our yard.

"Oh, isn't it a beauty?" I asked.

"Where is it?" I heard Craig cry.

"Over there, in the sky above the yellow house," I yelled. "Do you see it yet?"

"I would like to fly a jet like that one," said Craig.

"Let's try to save so that we can have our own plane when we grow up. Here's twenty cents to start," I said.

Just then, from down the street came the jingling of a bell and the blowing of a whistle. We both knew that it was Goody, the ice-cream man. His ice-cream bars were big and thick and creamy. Craig looked at me. "Why not?" I said. "It is very hot and dry."

As we ate the ice cream, Craig said "We'd better start soon to save for the airplane, or we'll be fifty years old before we get it."

"Yes," I said. "We'd better start early tomorrow."

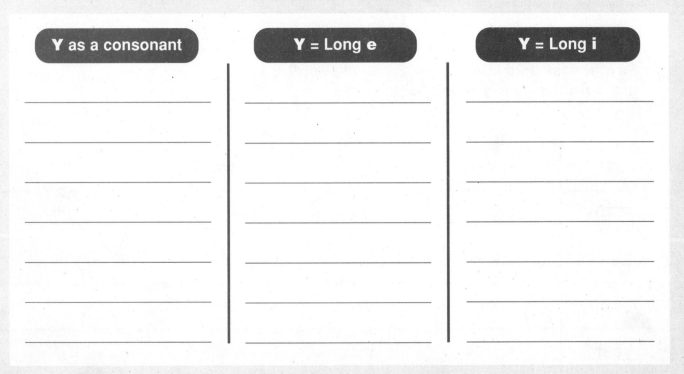

Y as a consonant	**Y = Long e**	**Y = Long i**

Home

Ask your child to think of a story using the words in the columns.

Name _____

AT THE CIRCUS

Clowns are usually the funniest people in the circus. They work hard and use their imaginations to make people laugh. Many clowns go to school for two months to create funny acts.

Each circus clown tries to be different from the others. They each have a special design for their white-painted faces. Some clowns wear extra large, funny shoes and use a loud horn to talk. Others tumble and pretend to be knocked down. The sillier the clown is, the harder people laugh! People are thrilled by the clown stars in a circus show.

1. _____ are the funniest people in the circus.

2. A clown works hard to _____ people _____.

3. Big shoes and a _____ face are some things the clown uses.

4. Clowns have a special _____ for their faces.

5. Some clowns pretend to be _____ down.

6. People are _____ by clowns.

7. These circus _____ are loved by all.

8. It's a great circus _____ when the clowns make people laugh.

 Why is imagination so important to a clown's success?

Phonics & Writing

You are a reporter for *Clowning Around* magazine. Write a report about how clowns make people laugh. Use these words and your own words.

clown
horn
laugh
paint
pants
practice
shoes
show
star
thrilled

Home

Ask your child to read his or her report to you

Name _____

 Circle the **ar, or, ir, ur,** or **er** in each word. Then find the word in the flowers with the same beginning letter and vowel sound. Write it on the line.

bark	bore	Burt	cord	dart	first	girlfriend
hurdle	leader	neither	purse	shore	startle	thirty

1. f i r _____

2. b u r n _____

3. l e t t e r _____

4. c o r n _____

5. h u r t _____

6. g i r l _____

7. d a r k _____

8. s t a r _____

9. b o r n _____

10. s h o r t _____

11. t h i r d _____

12. n e v e r _____

13. b a r n _____

14. p u r p l e _____

 Find the word in the ribbon that will complete the sentence. Write the word on the line.

15. My _____ has a green thumb.

16. She loves to work in her _____.

17. Our backyard is beautiful during the _____.

18. It is _____ with colorful flowers!

19. There are _____ and yellow and pink flowers.

20. Mom once won _____ place at a flower show.

21. Her eyes _____ as she received her prize.

bursting
garden
mother
orange
sparkled
summer
third

Lesson 36
R-controlled vowels

79

Read the sentences. Underline each word that contains ar, or, ir, ur, or er. Then write the words you underlined in the correct boxes below.

1. Rita made a special birthday card for a friend.
2. First she decorated it with blue and red stars.
3. Then she wrote a clever little verse.
4. In the morning, Rita hurried to the mailbox.
5. Darla received many surprises on Friday.
6. Mom and Dad gave her a purse, a curling brush, and a red sweater.
7. She got a yellow bird from Aunt Shirley.
8. Darla really likes the large and colorful greeting from Rita.

ir

er

or

ar

ur

Home

Ask your child to think of one more word to add to each gift box.

Name _____

Find and circle the hidden pictures. Then write each picture name on the lines below.

Word List

backpack	crow	glove	report	thirty
blanket	dragon	monkey	spoon	tiger
computer	flag	purse	swing	wheel

1. _____ 2. _____ 3. _____

4. _____ 5. _____ 6. _____

7. _____ 8. _____ 9. _____

10. _____ 11. _____ 12. _____

13. _____ 14. _____ 15. _____

Lesson 38
Review r-controlled vowels: Spelling

83

Phonics & Writing

Finish the story the monkey started. Use some of the words in the box and your own words.

favorite	garden	turn	overcoat	park	party
purple	short	thirty	tiger	turtle	yesterday

The funniest thing that ever happened to me was...

_____

_____

_____

_____

_____

_____

_____

Book Corner

Josephine's Catastrophes
by D. Marion
Silver Press, 1989

Follow the misadventures of Josephine, a cat with an eye for disaster!

Ask your child to read his or her humorous story to you.

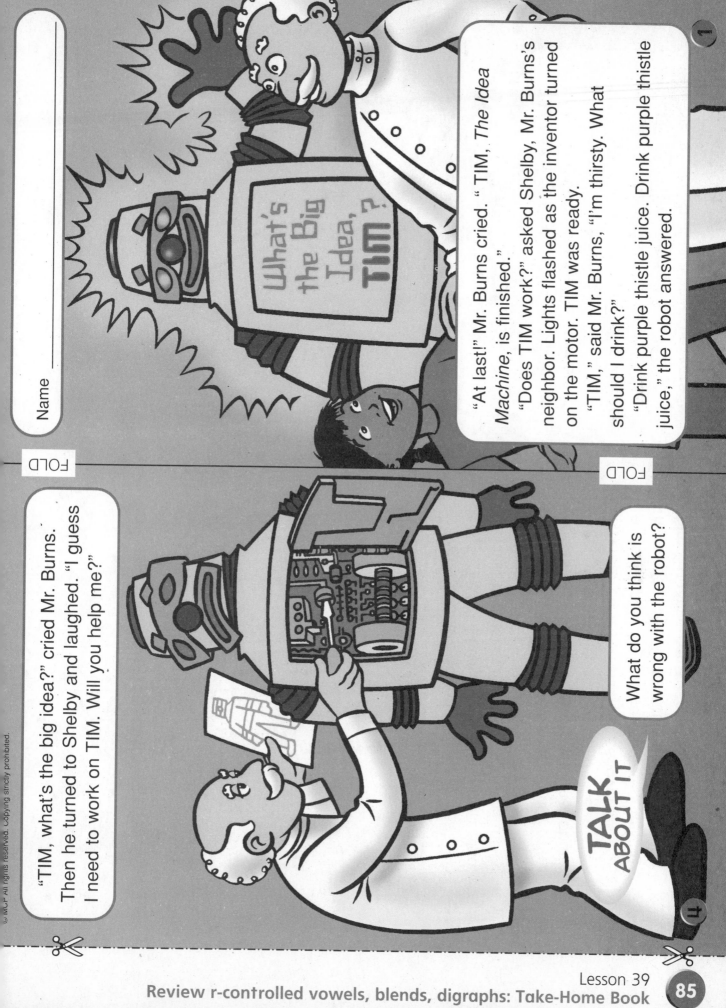

Name _____

FOLD

FOLD

What's the Big Idea, TIM?

"At last!" Mr. Burns cried. " TIM, *The Idea Machine*, is finished."

"Does TIM work?" asked Shelby, Mr. Burns's neighbor. Lights flashed as the inventor turned on the motor. TIM was ready.

"TIM," said Mr. Burns, "I'm thirsty. What should I drink?"

"Drink purple thistle juice. Drink purple thistle juice," the robot answered.

1

"TIM, what's the big idea?" cried Mr. Burns. Then he turned to Shelby and laughed. "I guess I need to work on TIM. Will you help me?"

What do you you think is wrong with the robot?

TALK ABOUT IT

4

"TIM has a special skill," said Mr. Burns. "If I use words with blends, he answers in words with the same blend."

"TIM," Mr. Burns continued, "it's snowing and blowing. What should I wear?" TIM lifted his shiny arms and said, "Wear your blue blazer and snappy snow sneakers."

FOLD

FOLD

"What should I do today?" Mr. Burns asked TIM. TIM winked at Shelby and said, "Shovel the steps. Push the snow off the shutters."

Just then TIM began to make funny noises. The lights flickered, and the robot's voice was a whisper.

"Wear purple thistle juice, shovel the roof," he said softly. The robot kept talking nonsense. Mr. Burns could not understand him. The inventor was very upset.

3

Lesson 39
Review r-controlled vowels, blends, digraphs: Take-Home Book

ON THE AIR

NEWS

Aahh

Sam's PLACE

Ed's MOVE-U-FAST

Ed's

> Look at this picture carefully. Can you name the eight careers?

THINK! Which job interests you most? Why?

Home Letter

Dear Family,

During this unit, your child will be learning about contractions in words with 's and 't, plurals with endings s and es, and suffixes er, est, ing, able, en, and y. As we learn to form new words, we will explore the world of work and learn about careers.

Contractions	Plurals	Suffixes	
it's	classes	thinner	washable
wouldn't	babies	largest	thicken
	leaves	hoping	frosty

At-Home Activities

Here are some activities you and your child might like to do together.

▶ Talk about the different careers represented on page 89. Discuss the kinds of tasks that these careers involve.

▶ Look for pictures in magazines and newspapers that illustrate career choices. Talk about all the kinds of work people do. With your child, write a list of occupations such as teacher, farmer, doctor, mechanic, artist, writer, veterinarian, and chef.

Book Corner

You and your child might enjoy reading these books together. Look for them in your local library.

Dog Days for Dudley
by Barbara Moe
Dudley tries to prove to his father that puppies are not too much trouble.

Uncle Jed's Barbershop
by Margaree King Mitchell
An elderly man finally realizes his dream of owning a business.

Sincerely,

Name _____

DEFINITION

A **contraction** is a short way of writing two words. It is formed by putting two words together and leaving out one or more letters. Use an apostrophe (') to show where something is left out.

I am = I'm   we will = we'll

► **Read each contraction. Write the two words that make each contraction. Then write the letter or letters that were left out.**

Contraction	Two Words	Letters Left Out
1. isn't		
2. there's		
3. haven't		
4. wouldn't		
5. you've		
6. it's		
7. let's		
8. don't		
9. they've		
10. couldn't		
11. he's		

► **Find the contraction in column B for each pair of words in column A and write it on the line.**

A		B	A		B
I am	_____	isn't	were not	_____	it's
is not	_____	I'm	would not	_____	wouldn't
we are	_____	I've	it is	_____	weren't
I have	_____	we're	did not	_____	didn't

A		B	A		B
you will	_____	let's	that is	_____	shouldn't
you are	_____	wasn't	they will	_____	aren't
let us	_____	we'll	will not	_____	that's
was not	_____	you'll	are not	_____	they'll
we will	_____	you're	should not	_____	won't

► **Complete each sentence using a contraction from the box below.**

we'll   It's   aren't   won't   I've

1. _____ going to be a fine day for a hike.

2. _____ been looking forward to it.

3. First _____ walk through the forest.

4. I hope the trails _____ muddy.

5. We _____ get home until evening.

Name _____

A Puzzling Situation

"There's T. rex!" said Sam excitedly as he and Alice ran up the stairs in the museum.

"How do scientists put these bones together?" asked Alice.

"It's like a puzzle," said a man behind them. "I'm Dr. West, museum paleontologist. I'd be happy to help you."

"Let's see triceratops!" exclaimed Alice as they walked to the next skeleton.

"Here's an interesting dinosaur," said Sam. "How did you know where each bone will fit?"

"That's a good question," said Dr. West. "It isn't easy, but we're able to use computers to help us with the bones we've found. Then we're ready to solve the puzzle!"

"Wouldn't that be fun to try!" said Alice.

"You're both welcome to watch us someday," said Dr. West. "You'd really enjoy it!"

"I think I'll be a paleontologist—he's a puzzle solver!" said Sam.

"Or she's a puzzle solver!" said Alice quickly. "I'd like to be a paleontologist, too!"

1. _____   2. _____   3. _____

4. _____   5. _____   6. _____

7. _____   8. _____   9. _____

10. _____   11. _____   12. _____

13. _____   14. _____   15. _____

16. _____   17. _____   18. _____

THINK! **Why is a scientist a puzzle solver?**

Write the two words that make each contraction.

1. I'm _____

2. aren't _____

3. can't _____

4. shouldn't _____

5. couldn't _____

6. didn't _____

7. he's _____

8. we'll _____

9. doesn't _____

10. let's _____

11. here's _____

12. you'll _____

13. I've _____

14. won't _____

15. you're _____

16. they've _____

17. she's _____

18. we've _____

19. I'll _____

20. it's _____

Write a story using five of the words listed above.

_____

_____

_____

_____

_____

_____

_____

Home Ask your child to read the story he or she wrote.

Name _____

> **Circle the word that names each picture. Then color the pictures that show more than one.**

RULE

When **s** or **es** is added to a word it forms the plural. Plural means "more than one." See how the ending **s** or **es** makes these words mean more than one.

| one pear | two pear**s** |
| one box | many box**es** |

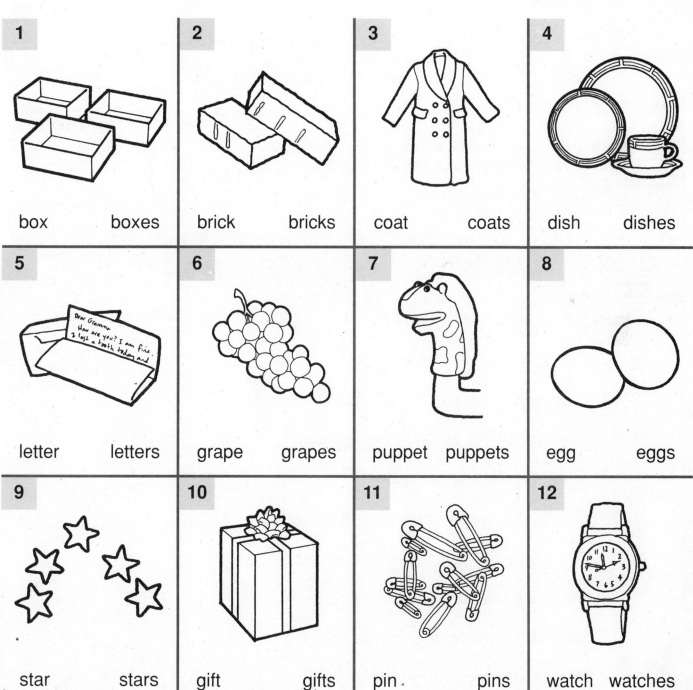

1. box   boxes

2. brick   bricks

3. coat   coats

4. dish   dishes

5. letter   letters

6. grape   grapes

7. puppet   puppets

8. egg   eggs

9. star   stars

10. gift   gifts

11. pin   pins

12. watch   watches

RULE

If a word ends in **ss, x, ch,** or **sh,** add the suffix **es** to make it mean more than one.

one porch	two porch**es**
one class	many class**es**
one fox	three fox**es**
one brush	some brush**es**

▶ **Write the plural form of the word in parentheses.**

1. five (cross) _____

2. some (glass) _____

3. those (box) _____

4. all (mix) _____

5. seven (dress) _____

6. few (church) _____

7. three (ax) _____

8. many (dish) _____

▶ **Underline the word in each sentence that means more than one. Then write its base word on the line.**

DEFINITION

The word to which a suffix is added is called the **base word**.

9. Kim is busy packing boxes. _____

10. She is using bunches of paper. _____

11. She carefully wraps the good dishes. _____

12. She puts paper around the glasses. _____

13. Then she packs her dresses. _____

14. Her favorite is the one with patches on it. _____

15. Kim marks her suitcase with crosses. _____

16. She does not pack her paintbrushes. _____

17. She ties them together in batches. _____

18. She needs them for her art classes. _____

Home Ask your child to say a base word and then add a suffix.

Name _____

Write the plural form of the word in parentheses.

1. three (cherry) _____

2. some (lily) _____

3. eight (fairy) _____

4. those (fly) _____

5. two (party) _____

6. nine (tray) _____

7. few (boy) _____

8. many (chimney) _____

9. four (day) _____

10. all (turkey) _____

Underline the word with a suffix in each sentence that means more than one. Then write its base word on the line.

11. Lucy went downtown to buy groceries. _____

12. She saw some puppies in a pet store window. _____

13. Two ladies worked in the store. _____

14. "May I pet the puppies?" Lucy asked. _____

15. One lady said, "They're as cute as monkeys." _____

16. "They're as stubborn as donkeys," said the other. _____

17. Lucy said, "They're as sweet as bunnies." _____

18. "They'll be sold in a few days," said the first lady. _____

19. Lucy asked, "Will you find homes for them in

nearby cities?" _____

20. "Yes, the puppies will each have a good home,"

the second lady said. _____

Look at each picture. Then read the word below the line. Change the word to mean more than one. Write the new word on the line.

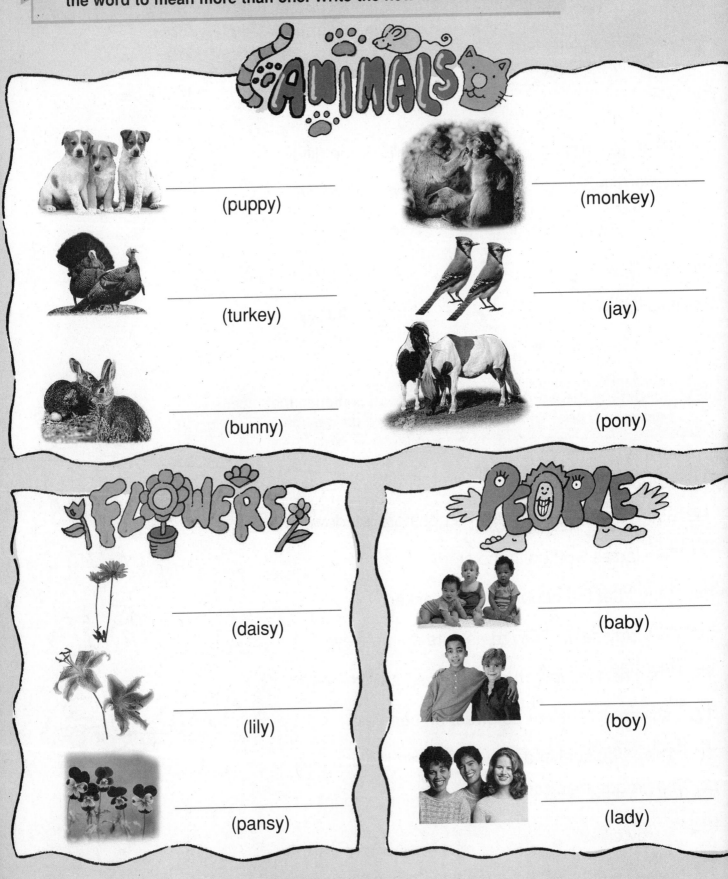

ANIMALS

_____
(puppy)

_____
(monkey)

_____
(turkey)

_____
(jay)

_____
(bunny)

_____
(pony)

FLOWERS

PEOPLE

_____
(daisy)

_____
(baby)

_____
(lily)

_____
(boy)

_____
(pansy)

_____
(lady)

Lesson 44
Suffixes -s and -es with words ending in y

Name _____

RULE

If a word ends in **f** or **fe,** change the **f** or **fe** to **v** before adding the suffix **es.**

one thief several thie**ves**
one life nine li**ves**

▶ **Write the plural form of the word in parentheses on the line.**

1. these (leaf) _____

2. six (calf) _____

3. those (wolf) _____

4. few (knife) _____

5. four (shelf) _____

6. several (elf) _____

7. two (half) _____

8. few (wife) _____

9. ten (thief) _____

10. many (life) _____

▶ **Write a word from the boxes below to complete each sentence. Then write its base word on the line.**

calves   knives   leaves
scarves   shelves   wives

lives   loaves
wolves

11. Long ago, pioneers led hard _____.   _____

12. The men chopped wood to make _____.   _____

13. They built barns for the cow and _____.   _____

14. They had to protect them from wild _____.   _____

15. Pioneer _____ worked as hard as their husbands.   _____

16. Each week they baked _____ of bread.   _____

17. They made medicine from _____ and roots.   _____

18. At night, the women knitted warm _____.   _____

19. The men sharpened their _____ beside the fire.   _____

Read each clue. Find the word in the box that matches the clue. Then write the word in the crossword puzzle.

elf	thieves	scarves	foxes	loaves
wife	scarf	turkeys	lives	wolf
shelves	axes	elves	car	

Across

1. singular form of elves
4. plural form of thief
7. plural form of scarf
9. singular form of wives
12. plural form of fox
13. plural form of turkey

Down

2. plural form of life
3. plural form of shelf
5. plural form of elf
6. plural form of loaf
8. singular form of scarves
9. singular form of wolves
10. plural form of ax
11. singular form of cars

Lesson 45
Suffix -es with words ending in f and fe

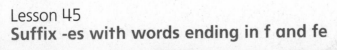

Home

Name _____

Read each word. Make new words by adding the suffixes **s**, **ed**, and **ing**. Write the new words in the correct columns.

s	ed	ing
1. cook		
2. jump		
3. pick		
4. clean		
5. help		
6. learn		
7. play		

Write the base word for each of the following words.

8. eggs _____		**16.** hats _____
9. lifts _____		**17.** makes _____
10. washed _____		**18.** dreamed _____
11. worked _____		**19.** burns _____
12. spelling _____		**20.** stacked _____
13. started _____		**21.** looking _____
14. dressed _____		**22.** opening _____
15. runs _____		**23.** reading _____

RULES

The suffix **er** may be used to compare two things. The suffix **est** may be used to compare more than two things.

Read each sentence. Add er or est to each word below the line. Write the new word on the line.

1. Lisa is _____ than her sister Nancy.
   (tall)

2. Nancy is _____ than Lisa.
   (old)

3. Their little sister Joy is

   the _____ .
   (young)

4. Joy is also the _____ .
   (short)

5. "Lisa may be tall," says Joy, "but I'm

   _____ than she is!"

   (smart)

RULE

The suffix **er** sometimes means *a person who*. A teacher is a person who teaches.

Add the suffix er to each word. Write the new word on the line.

6. teach _____

7. perform _____

8. sing _____

9. play _____

10. work _____

11. report _____

12. farm _____

13. print _____

Ask your child to use the words on the lines above to make sentences.

Home

Name _____

> **Circle each word that ends in a single consonant. Then add the suffixes to make new words.**

RULE

When a word with a short vowel ends in a single consonant, usually double the consonant before adding a suffix that begins with a vowel.

| pet | pet**ted** | pet**ting** |
| thin | thin**ner** | thin**nest** |

ed   ing

1. tag _____ _____
2. rip _____ _____
3. jump _____ _____
4. nap _____ _____

er   est

5. big _____ _____
6. fat _____ _____
7. cold _____ _____
8. hot _____ _____

> **Circle the word with a suffix in each sentence. Write its base word on the line.**

9. Today was the hottest day of the summer. _____

10. Joe slept longer than he did yesterday. _____

11. A frog skipped by Joe's toes. _____

12. He let out a snore and sent it hopping. _____

Doubling the final consonant with suffixes

Complete each sentence by adding the correct suffix to the word in parentheses. Write the word on the line.

1. Ed was tired of _____ on the bench. (sit)

2. He _____ the coach to let him play. (beg)

3. "I'm _____ you in the game," said the coach. (put)

4. On the first try, Ed _____ the ball. (fan)

5. Then he _____ the ball past the pitcher. (bat)

6. He began _____ and reached home plate. (run)

7. "Ed's our _____ player!" said the coach. (hot)

8. Ed was proud to be a _____. (win)

	RUNS	HITS	ERRORS	1	2	3	4	5	6	7	8	9
Home	8	10	4	1	0	1	1	2	1	2		
Visitor	5	9	3	1	2	0	1	0	1			

Write the base word for each of the following words.

9. shopper _____

10. swimmer _____

11. tagged _____

12. stopper _____

13. tipping _____

14. petted _____

15. dripping _____

16. rubbed _____

17. chopper _____

18. tapped _____

19. cutting _____

20. bigger _____

21. quitting _____

22. hopping _____

23. hitting _____

24. biggest _____

Lesson 47
Doubling the final consonant with suffixes

Name a base word and ask your child to spell the word with a suffix.

Name _____

Read each sentence. Add the suffix to each word. Then circle the word that completes the sentence.

1

May-ling _____ her music every afternoon.

practice + es = _____   bake + es = _____

2

Fluffy is the _____ cat I've ever seen!

ripe + est = _____   cute + est = _____

3

Chef Edna _____ cucumbers for a salad.

shine + es = _____   slice + es = _____

4

Dale makes up stories because she wants to

be a _____.

write + er = _____   dive + er = _____

5

Mike has a job _____ leaves for his neighbor.

hide + ing = _____   rake + ing = _____

6

Carlos _____ an insect for his Future Scientists project.

examine + ed = _____   baste + ed = _____

Make new words by adding the suffixes shown below.
Write the new words in the correct columns.

	es	**ed**	**ing**
1. skate			
2. race			
3. smile			
4. lace			
5. glaze			
6. place			

	er	**est**
7. fine		
8. ripe		
9. cute		
10. pure		
11. tame		
12. nice		

TO SKATE RACE

Home

Say a base word and a suffix and ask your child to spell the word.

Name _____

1. taking _____
2. hiding _____
3. shining _____
4. chased _____
5. bravest _____
6. used _____
7. smiles _____
8. bakes _____
9. traced _____
10. hoping _____
11. safer _____
12. largest _____

▶ **Read each sentence. Circle the word that has a suffix and write its base word on the line.**

13. Carl was shaking his bank.

14. "I need a larger baseball mitt," he said.

15. "I want the latest model."

16. Nothing rattled when he shook the bank.

17. He had spent almost all of his money on ice skates.

18. "I only practiced on them once," he said.

19. "Mom told me the lake seldom freezes."

20. Carl thought baseball was the finest game.

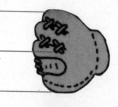

21. He could have used the mitt all year.

22. "I should have been wiser," he said.

Lesson 49
Suffixes with words ending in e   107

Read each sentence. Complete the sentence by adding the correct suffix to the word in parentheses. Write the new word on the line.

1. Dan has a little brother _____ Tim.   (name)

2. Dan usually _____ to baby-sit with Tim.   (like)

3. One day Dan's parents _____ to go to a wedding.   (arrange)

4. Dan had planned to go ice _____ that day.   (skate)

5. His parents _____ he'd baby-sit with Tim.   (hope)

6. He hated _____ his plans.   (change)

7. Then Mother had an idea that _____ the day.   (save)

8. "How about _____ Tim with you?" she asked.   (take)

9. Dan _____ that it was a good idea.   (agree)

10. "Taking Tim is _____ than not going," said Dan.   (nice)

11. Tim was happy to be _____ along.   (invite)

12. "You'll be the _____ kid on skates!" said Dan.   (cute)

 What do you think happened?

Home   Ask your child to read the completed sentences.

Name _____

Phonics & Reading

▶ **Read the paragraph. Then write the correct word on the line to complete each sentence.**

A Traveling Writer

My name is Aggie Clifford. When I grow up, I want to be a travel writer like my aunt Agatha Clifford. She writes books and stories about Africa. Her collection of African animal guides is one of the finest anywhere. It would be exciting to take trips to faraway places. Aunt Agatha is often invited to speak about her trips and her books.

African elephants are the subject of her latest book. During her last trip to Africa she saw many elephants grazing near a watering hole. They used their ears as fans. Did you know that African elephants are the world's largest land mammals? Aunt Agatha was surprised one day when she heard rumbling sounds. But it was only the elephants looking for water!

1. Agatha Clifford is a travel _____.

2. She _____ books and stories.

3. It would be_____ to take trips to faraway places.

4. She is often _____ to speak about her trips and books.

5. Her _____ book is about elephants.

6. She saw elephants _____ near a watering hole.

7. They used their _____ as fans.

8. Elephants are the world's_____ land mammals.

Why do you think Ms. Clifford is a good writer?

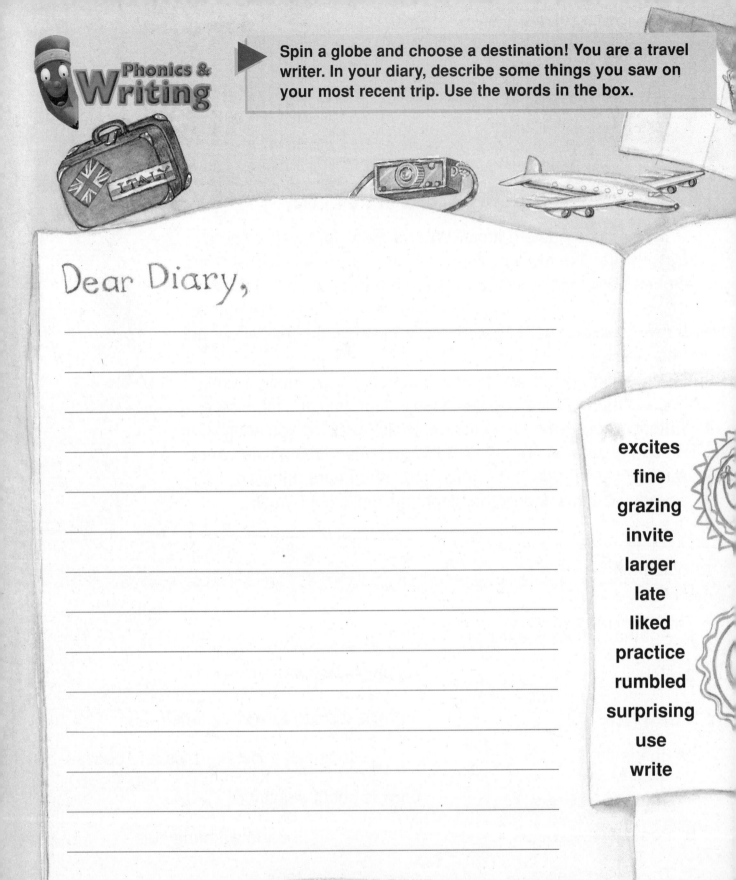

Spin a globe and choose a destination! You are a travel writer. In your diary, describe some things you saw on your most recent trip. Use the words in the box.

Dear Diary,

_____

_____

_____

_____

_____

_____

_____

_____

_____

_____

_____

_____

_____

_____

_____

excites
fine
grazing
invite
larger
late
liked
practice
rumbled
surprising
use
write

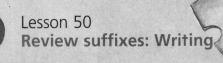

Home
Ask your child to read his or her diary page.

Name _____

▶ **Read each sentence. Add the suffix ful, less, ly, or ness to the word below the line. Write the new word on the line.**

1. Jan was sick, and food seemed _____ to her.
   (taste)

2. It was _____ for Jan to swallow.
   (pain)

3. "Your face is pale and looks _____," said Mother.
   (color)

4. "I hope the doctor comes _____."
   (quick)

5. Jan's _____ turned out to be mumps.
   (ill)

6. "It's not too serious," the doctor said _____.
   (kind)

7. "You must be _____ to get plenty of rest."
   (care)

8. "I don't like having mumps," Jan said _____.
   (sad)

9. "Take a _____ of medicine," said Mother.
   (spoon)

10. "Then I will _____ read to you."
    (glad)

THINK! **What else can Jan do?**

Lesson 51
Suffixes -ful, -less, -ly, -ness

111

Read each word. Make new words by adding the suffixes. Write the new words in the correct columns.

	er	est	ly	ness
1. sick				
2. neat				
3. loud				
4. quick				
5. bright				

	ful	less
6. care		
7. thank		
8. pain		
9. hope		
10. help		

Write the base word for each of the words below.

11. kindness _____   12. gladly _____

13. smaller _____   14. harmless _____

15. coldest _____   16. spoonful _____

17. useful _____   18. sadness _____

19. homeless _____   20. taller _____

Lesson 51
Suffixes -er, -est, -ly, -ness, -ful, -less

Home

Choose a base word and a suffix and ask your child to say the new word.

Name _____

1. sleep _____

2. frost _____

3. rain _____

4. thirst _____

5. air _____

6. dust _____

7. crank _____

8. rock _____

▶ **Read each sentence. Circle the word that correctly completes the sentence. Write the word on the line.**

9. Tom got out his old _____ sled.

   rusty   thirsty

10. It was the first _____ day of winter.

    sleepy   snowy

11. It was so _____ Tom's hat blew off.

    lumpy   windy

12. It blew his _____ hair into his eyes.

    curly   cranky

13. Sledding would be _____.

    airy   tricky

14. Tom pulled his sled up the _____ hill.

    bumpy   dreamy

15. His sled made a _____ sound.

    squeaky   frosty

16. It was a _____ ride down the hill.

    rainy   speedy

▶ **Read each word and write its base word on the line beside it.**

1. washable _____
2. harden _____
3. darken _____
4. frighten _____
5. brighten _____
6. straighten _____

7. soften _____
8. sinkable _____
9. writable _____
10. breakable _____
11. likable _____
12. lovable _____

▶ **Read each clue. Write the answer in the crossword puzzle.**

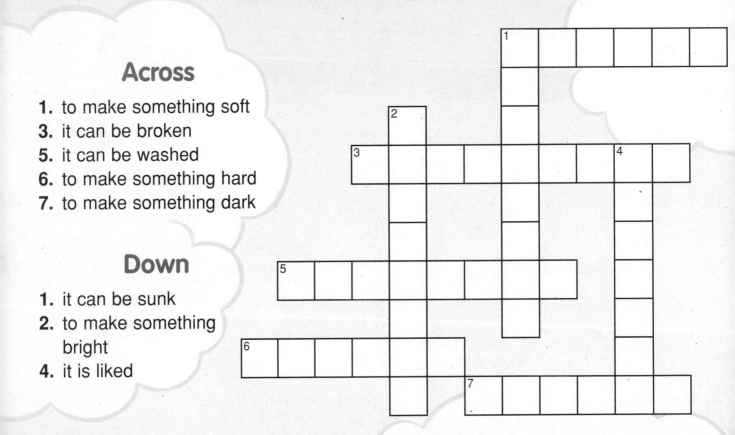

Across

1. to make something soft
3. it can be broken
5. it can be washed
6. to make something hard
7. to make something dark

Down

1. it can be sunk
2. to make something bright
4. it is liked

Lesson 52
Suffixes -en, and -able

Ask your child to name the base word in numbers 1-12.

Circle each word that has the suffix shown in the box.
Then write the base word on the line.

Suffix y

1. It had not rained, so the playground was dusty. _____

2. The school children felt lucky to be outside. _____

3. The smooth soil was not too rocky to run races. _____

4. After playing, everyone felt hot and sticky. _____

5. Now the children wished it was cold and frosty. _____

Suffix en

6. Natalie began to straighten the baby's bedroom. _____

7. The blanket she had washed to soften was folded. _____

8. She pulled down the shades to darken the room. _____

9. The very dark room might frighten a tiny baby. _____

10. She raised the shades to brighten the room again. _____

Suffix able

11. Jack sorted clothes that were no longer wearable. _____

12. He placed the washable clothes in one pile. _____

13. Some clothes were suitable for his little brother. _____

14. Others would be usable for charities. _____

Divide each word into syllables. Write the syllables on the lines.

RULE

A suffix that has a vowel sound forms a syllable by itself.

1. playing _____

2. lighten _____

3. spoonful _____

4. gladly _____

5. needed _____

6. playful _____

7. cheerful _____

8. lovely _____

9. shining _____

10. loudest _____

11. useless _____

12. darkness _____

13. training _____

14. eating _____

15. homeless _____

16. blooming _____

17. careful _____

18. laughing _____

19. patches _____

20. painting _____

21. wiper _____

22. snowy _____

23. hopeful _____

24. neatness _____

25. slowly _____

26. waiting _____

27. careless _____

28. rainy _____

29. brighten _____

30. useful _____

116

Lesson 53
Syllables in words with suffixes

Home

Ask your child to say the word you point to and tell the number of syllables.

Name _____

In each box match the base word in the first column with
a suffix in the second column to make a new word. Write
the word on the line.

1

luck	able	_____
cold	y	_____
wash	ful	_____
hope	est	_____

2

fly	less	_____
loud	ing	_____
peach	est	_____
meat	es	_____

3

safe	y	_____
church	ing	_____
health	ly	_____
say	es	_____

4

teach	less	_____
home	ed	_____
land	ful	_____
cup	er	_____

5

sink	y	_____
rest	ed	_____
cloud	en	_____
fright	able	_____

6

sleep	ful	_____
light	able	_____
spoon	y	_____
clean	en	_____

7

ax	ly	_____
sad	y	_____
use	ful	_____
rain	es	_____

8

fox	ed	_____
hammer	ness	_____
neat	able	_____
break	es	_____

Write the number of syllables in each word.

1. knives ___   2. plays ___   3. shelves ___

4. boxes ___   5. churches ___   6. tagging ___

7. cleaned ___   8. parties ___   9. jumped ___

10. hopeful ___   11. thirsty ___   12. loving ___

13. loudly ___   14. chimneys ___   15. sleepy ___

16. painful ___   17. darken ___   18. sickness ___

19. receiving ___   20. foxes ___   21. hiking ___

22. wives ___   23. days ___   24. harmless ___

25. purest ___   26. glasses ___   27. leaves ___

28. shining ___   29. running ___   30. gladly ___

31. cherries ___   32. cooking ___   33. patches ___

34. begging ___   35. rolling ___   36. wolves ___

37. skated ___   38. weakest ___   39. snowy ___

40. straighten ___   41. homeless ___   42. smoothest ___

43. wiper ___   44. axes ___   45. picked ___

46. turkeys ___   47. whitest ___   48. sinkable ___

49. breakable ___   50. raking ___   51. daisies ___

Lesson 54
Syllables in words with suffixes

Home

Name a word and ask your child to tell
you the number of syllables.

Name _____

 Say and spell each word. Write the words on the note pad where they belong.

Word List

bushes	chopped	foxes	gives	losses
lunches	nicer	padded	pencils	pillows
running	saved	tagging	takes	writing

Plurals

_____

_____

_____

_____

_____

Base Word with Final e

_____

_____

_____

_____

Base Word Ending with Single Consonant

_____

_____

_____

_____

Write a complete sentence using a different word from each column.

1. _____

2. _____

3. _____

Phonics & Writing

If you could interview one person about his or her job, whom would it be? Write the questions you would ask that person. Use some of the words in the box.

bravest	careful	cheerful	doesn't	finest
friendly	greatly	helpful	I've	isn't
kindness	quickly	there's	they've	you've

Book Corner

Take It Apart Plane
by Chris Oxlade

Have you ever wanted to be a pilot? Find out how planes work in this interesting book.

Home

Have your child interview family members about their jobs.

Name _____

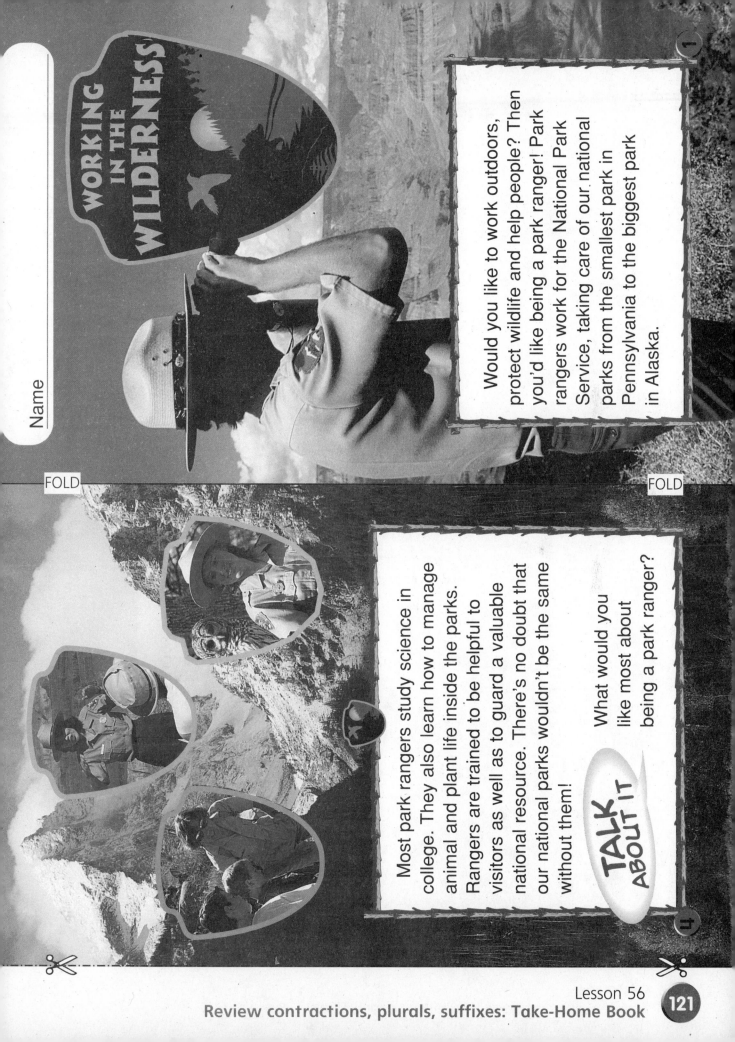

WORKING IN THE WILDERNESS

Would you like to work outdoors, protect wildlife and help people? Then you'd like being a park ranger! Park rangers work for the National Park Service, taking care of our national parks from the smallest park in Pennsylvania to the biggest park in Alaska.

1

FOLD   FOLD

Most park rangers study science in college. They also learn how to manage animal and plant life inside the parks. Rangers are trained to be helpful to visitors as well as to guard a valuable national resource. There's no doubt that our national parks wouldn't be the same without them!

TALK ABOUT IT

What would you like most about being a park ranger?

4

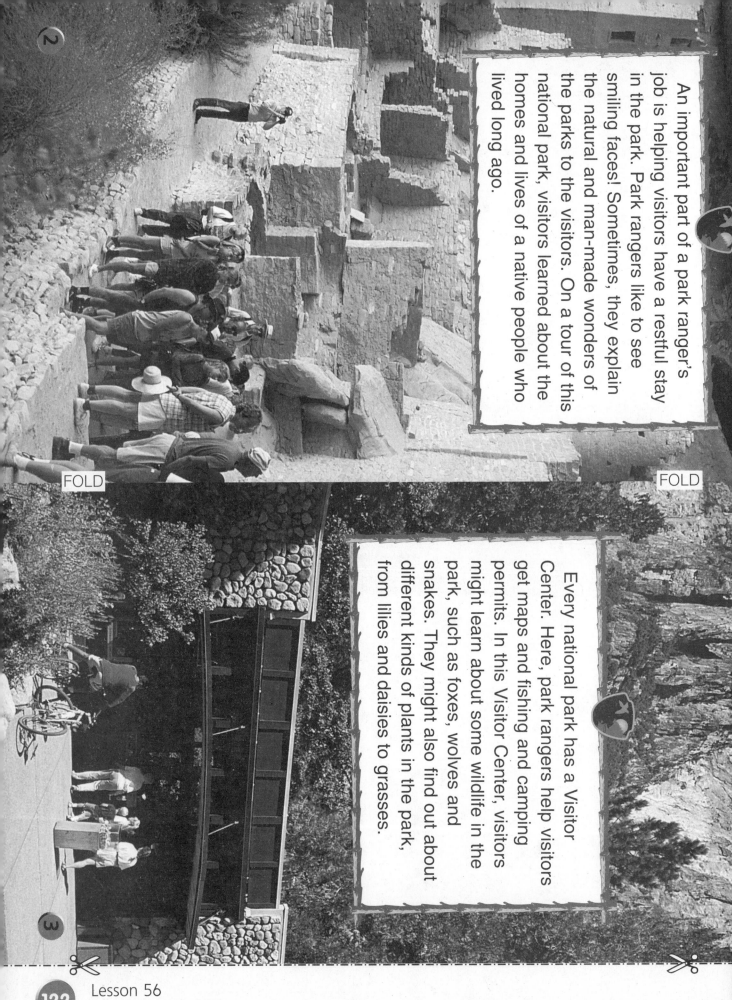

An important part of a park ranger's job is helping visitors have a restful stay in the park. Park rangers like to see smiling faces! Sometimes, they explain the natural and man-made wonders of the parks to the visitors. On a tour of this national park, visitors learned about the homes and lives of a native people who lived long ago.

Every national park has a Visitor Center. Here, park rangers help visitors get maps and fishing and camping permits. In this Visitor Center, visitors might learn about some wildlife in the park, such as foxes, wolves and snakes. They might also find out about different kinds of plants in the park, from lilies and daisies to grasses.

FOLD

FOLD

2

3

Lesson 56
Review contractions, plurals, suffixes: Take-Home Book

UNIT 5

Vowel Pairs, Digraphs, Diphthongs

Theme: By the Sea!

In the Deep Blue Sea

What do you see in the deep blue sea?

I see . . .

A starfish, a rainbow trout,

A sea turtle and a shark's mouth,

And a sea horse, too.

I can find them . . . can you?

But animals, too, live near the sea . . .

The furry beaver and the silky seal,

A proud penguin and a puffin, too.

Animals and fish in waters blue,

I can find them . . . can you?

▶ **Find and name the fish and animals in this picture of life in and near the water.**

THINK! **What other kinds of fish and animals could you add to this picture?**

Home Letter

Dear Family,

In the next few weeks, your child will be learning to read and write words with vowel pairs (**oa** as in b**oa**t), vowel digraphs (**aw** as in cl**aw**), and vowel diphthongs (**oi** as in c**oi**ns). As we explore words with these sounds, we'll learn about animals and fish that live in or near the water.

oa	aw	oi

boat	**claw**	**coins**

At-Home Activities

You and your child might like to do the following activities together.

▶ Read the poem on page 125. Then ask your child to identify the fish and animals in the picture.

▶ Look for pictures in magazines and books of other animals that live in or near the water and make a list of their names. Then create a scrapbook of animals that your child likes.

▶ If you live near an aquarium, plan to visit and get information about fish and animals that make their homes in or near the water.

Book Corner

You and your child might enjoy reading these books together. Look for them in your local library.

Keeper for the Sea
by Kimberley Brady

A man teaches his granddaughter to fish and to respect the ocean and its creatures.

Walk by the Seashore
by Caroline Arnold

This book introduces various plants and creatures found along the seashore.

Sincerely,

Name _____

RULE

In a **vowel pair** two vowels come together to make one long vowel sound. When one syllable has a vowel pair, the first vowel stands for the long sound and the second vowel is silent.

b**oa**t   tr**ee**   p**ie**
l**ea**f   tr**ai**n   tr**ay**

Find the word in the box that will complete the sentence. Write the word on the line.

coat	dries	feels	may	paint	board
seals	shows	soaks	teach	tries	

1. Joan will _____ Kay to paint walls today.

2. First she _____ Kay how to fix the cracks.

3. Kay practices on a _____ .

4. She _____ to fill the holes with plaster.

5. When the wet plaster _____ , the holes are all filled.

6. Next she _____ the holes with more plaster.

7. Then Kay is ready to _____ .

8. Joan shows her how to put on the first _____ of paint.

9. The clean brush _____ up the green paint.

10. Kay _____ that she has done the work well.

11. Joan _____ let Kay finish the job.

THINK! Do you think Kay will finish the job? Why or why not?

Read each sentence. Find a word or words from the box that best completes each sentence. Write each word on the line.

beans	boat	cool	good	great	new	pie
pool	rope	sail	snails	read	soap	tow

1. Before we went to the beach, we washed our hands

   with _____ on a _____.

2. Mom gave us cold green _____ for lunch.

3. Dad got some _____ on his new shorts.

4. Robbie said it was a _____ day for a _____.

5. Jill said, "I'm going to wear my _____ swimsuit."

6. Mr. Burns had to _____ his new _____.

7. At the beach, we put _____ in a pail.

8. The beach was hot but it was _____ by the pool.

9. Grandma said, "I'm going to _____ a _____ book."

10. Grandpa said, "I'm going to sleep by the _____."

THINK! How do you know if it's a good day for the beach?

Lesson 58
Vowel pairs: Words in context

Home

Ask your child to name the vowel pairs in the words in the word box.

Name _____

Underline each word with a vowel pair in the sentences. Write the words on the lines at the bottom of the page.

1. Ann and Ted went to the stable to feed the horses.

2. The horses like to eat oats from the large pail.

3. Ann and Ted tried to ride at least once a week.

4. The plan for today was to go riding on the trail.

5. It was chilly, and the leaves were changing colors.

6. There were many pretty trees and bushes.

7. Ann and Ted stopped for lunch by a stream.

8. A toad jumped along the grassy bank.

9. The water flowed slowly over the huge rocks.

10. Ann put her feet into the cold water.

11. Ted lay on the grass and gazed at the sky.

12. A tiny boat with a red sail drifted by them.

13. Ann and Ted sat and dreamed.

14. Then it was three o'clock and time to go home.

_____   _____   _____

_____   _____   _____

_____   _____   _____

_____   _____   _____

_____   _____   _____

_____   _____   _____

THINK! If Ann and Ted rode on the same trail 3 months later, what would they see?

Fill in the circle beside the word that will complete the sentence. Write the word on the line.

1. Jason and Jeff played in the _____ all day. ○ snow ○ soap

2. Making a snowman made them _____ very cold. ○ foam ○ feel

3. They went inside to play with Jeff's _____. ○ tree ○ train

4. It felt good to remove their winter _____. ○ coats ○ coal

5. Jeff's dog wagged his _____ to greet them. ○ tie ○ tail

6. Jeff's mom made some hot apple cider for a _____. ○ treat ○ tried

7. They had to _____ on the carpet to play. ○ kneel ○ know

8. A _____ on the train came off the track. ○ when ○ wheel

9. Jason _____ to help Jeff fix it. ○ tray ○ tried

10. Soon it was able to _____ along the rails. ○ coast ○ crow

11. The train ran smoothly the rest of the _____. ○ deal ○ day

---

Read each clue. Then write the answer that contains the given vowel pair.

12. something to sail in   oa _____

13. something we do to shoelaces   ie _____

14. something that runs on tracks   ai _____

15. something a rooster can do   ow _____

16. something we do at recess   ay _____

17. something that grows on a tree ea _____

Home Help your child think of other words with vowel pairs **oa, ie, ai, ow, ay, ea.**

Name _____

Circle each word that has the vowel digraph **oo** or **ea**. Then write the words in the correct columns.

1. Mike and Joe looked at the clock and saw that it was noon.

2. They stood up and left the classroom.

3. The weather was cool, so they grabbed their jackets.

4. They were ready to play a good game of football.

5. Mike threw the heavy ball, and it sailed over Joe's head.

6. The ball took a sudden turn toward the school wall.

7. Mike watched with dread as it went toward a window.

8. At the last minute, Joe scooped up the ball.

oo as in **book**	**oo** as in **pool**	**ea** as in **bread**

THINK! **What would the boys have done if they had broken a window?**

Lesson 60
Vowel digraphs

131

Find the word in the box that will complete the sentence. Write the word on the line.

| bread | breakfast | headlines | heavy | ready | weather |

1. Heather and Sid eat a large _____ every day.

2. They have _____ and jam with their milk and cereal.

3. Sid reads all the _____ in the newspaper first.

4. The _____ report said that it would snow later.

5. Heather and Sid put on their _____ coats and boots.

6. Now they are _____ for their long walk to school.

Find the word in the box that will complete the sentence. Write the word on the line.

| eight | eighteen | neighbor | veins | weighs | weight |

7. Lauren's health class grew from sixteen students to _____.

8. Her _____, Mrs. Parkhurst, is the health teacher.

9. She teaches that _____ carry blood to the heart.

10. Lauren learns how to read a scale to find her _____.

11. It shows that Lauren _____ sixty pounds.

12. Lauren gained _____ pounds since last year.

Lesson 60
Vowel digraphs: Words in context

▶ **Circle each word that has the vowel digraph aw, au, or ei. Then write the words in the correct columns below.**

1. Claude sat on the lawn under an oak tree and yawned.
2. Although it was August, he thought about a sleigh in the snow.
3. It would be awesome to see eight tiny reindeer.
4. He watched an ant crawl up a vein on a leaf.
5. He dreamed of being an author and drawing pictures.
6. The whistle of a distant freight train woke him from his dream.
7. He felt naughty because his chores were not done.

aw as in **saw**   **au** as in **caught**   **ei** as in **eight**

_____   _____   _____
_____   _____   _____
_____   _____   _____
_____   _____   _____
_____   _____   _____

Circle each word that has a vowel digraph. Then write the words in the correct column.

1. In August Paul mowed the lawn at his uncle's big farm.

2. He liked to start in the morning when it was cool.

3. Sometimes he hauled bales of straw to the barn.

4. His uncle often helped him lift the heavy load.

5. During the hot afternoon, his head began to sweat.

6. He met his neighbors at the swimming pool.

7. Before diving, he looked for the deepest water.

8. By eight o'clock he was so tired that he began to yawn.

9. He went home to read a good book about weight lifting.

oo as in **book**	**oo** as in **moon**	**ei** as in **sleigh**

ea as in **thread**	**aw** as in **saw**	**au** as in **auto**

THINK!

Do you think Paul likes to work on the farm? Why or why not?

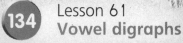

134 Lesson 61
Vowel digraphs

Home

Help your child think of another word
for each vowel digraph.

Name _____

Read the clues. Find the word that matches each clue.
Write the word in the puzzle.

brook   eel   eight   snail   seaweed
coast   sailfish   prawn   sea horse   oyster

Across

2. a food from the sea that is like a shrimp

5. a fish with a long slippery body

6. a slow-moving sea animal with a coiled shell

8. the number after seven

9. a small fish with a head like a horse

Down

1. a small stream

3. a large fish with a big fin

4. the land along the sea

7. a sea animal with soft body with a hard shell

10. one of many kinds of water plants

Underline each word in the sentences below that contains a vowel pair or a vowel digraph. Write the words in the correct columns.

1. The freezing rain and sleet beat on the windowpane.
2. The streets looked awfully icy for a March day.
3. The news said a yellow school bus was caught in a ditch.
4. The news headline said, "No school today because of snow."
5. The weather wasn't good for a sleigh ride.
6. My mother said that I could play with my neighbor, Paula.
7. I helped Paula bake raisin bread instead.
8. She showed me that it is easy to have fun.

Vowel Pair	Vowel Digraph
_____	_____
_____	_____
_____	_____
_____	_____
_____	_____
_____	_____
_____	_____
_____	_____
_____	_____

Lesson 62
Vowel pairs and digraphs: Review

Home

Ask your child to list words with vowel pairs and vowel digraphs.

Name _____

Phonics & Reading

Read the journal entry. Then write words with vowel pairs and vowel digraphs to complete each sentence.

February 14

Our sightseeing boat floated across the blue and green waters of the bay. Then we saw them—the great gray whales. As we came near one, I leaned over the side of the boat. The whale's great brown eye seemed to be looking right at me! Her head followed my every move. I wanted to reach out and touch her, but I was afraid she would leave.

Suddenly, the ocean seemed to boil as the whale dove under our boat. Then the whale lifted us out of the water with her head as if we were weightless. We slid down her side and swirled around and around. She was playing with us like a bathtub toy! Luckily, she saw something else to play with and she left us alone.

1. The waters of the lagoon were _____ and _____ .

2. Then we saw the great _____ whales.

3. The author saw the whale's _____ eye.

4. The water seemed to _____ when the whale dove under the surface.

5. The whale lifted the boat with her _____ .

6. The boat seemed to be _____ .

7. The whale was _____ with the boat.

8. She treated the boat like a _____ .

THINK! How do you think the tourists felt when the whale lifted them up?

Phonics & Writing

Have you ever spent a special day by the sea? (If not, make one up!) Write a journal entry telling about your real or imagined day. Some of the words in the box may help you.

blue	coast	eight	flowed	green
looked	play	ready	saw	tried

Lesson 63
Review vowel pairs and digraphs: Writing

Home

Invite your child to read the journal entry aloud.

TALK
ABOUT IT

What do you
think a beaver
does if trees are
not near the
place where it
builds its house?

FOLD

FOLD

Name

BEAVERS
ARE GREAT BUILDERS

Beavers have thick brown fur,
small forepaws, and a wide, flat tail
that can be up to 12 inches long.
These furry animals can swim up to
2 miles per hour, using their webbed
back feet as paddles and their tails
as rudders. A beaver can stay
underwater for 15 minutes without
coming up for air!

Grass and moss are then added to the tree branches, and everything is joined together with mud. The first floor is above the water with a hole in the roof for air. The entrance to the lodge is underwater, though, so that when the water freezes the beavers can still enter their house.

FOLD FOLD

Beavers look for a place on a riverbank, lake, or pond to build a house or lodge. Tree branches from poplar or aspen trees are usually used to build it. To cut down the trees, beavers use their powerful, chisel-like teeth to gnaw through trees up to 5 feet 7 inches thick! To split the wood from a large tree, two beavers will help each other cut it into smaller pieces.

Lesson 67
Review vowel pairs, digraphs, diphthongs: Take-Home Book

Name _____

▶ **Read the word in the box. Fill in the circle in front of the word that has the same vowel sound.**

1. awning
○ meat   ○ school   ○ taught

2. bread
○ led   ○ sea   ○ say

3. goose
○ scout   ○ tool   ○ book

4. weigh
○ feel   ○ boil   ○ late

5. clown
○ paid   ○ loud   ○ boat

6. know
○ room   ○ chew   ○ goat

7. green
○ teach   ○ bread   ○ vein

8. joy
○ jaw   ○ join   ○ wood

9. pause
○ lawn   ○ eight   ○ leap

10. soak
○ shout   ○ soy   ○ know

11. play
○ main   ○ crawl   ○ boy

12. mouse
○ crook   ○ broom   ○ brown

13. leaves
○ trees   ○ vein   ○ threw

14. good
○ boil   ○ bloom   ○ look

15. sail
○ stay   ○ draw   ○ tried

16. coin
○ toy   ○ shook   ○ soon

Circle the word that best completes each sentence. Write the word on the line.

1. My brother and I _____ a riddle game.   played   plowed

2. We _____ turns making up animal riddles.   took   tied

3. What has a curly tail and says _____?   oats   oink

4. What is brown when small and green when

   _____?   grass   grown

5. What can fly and says _____?   chime   cheep

6. What is a large black bird that makes a sound

   like _____?   caw   coo

7. What is small, yellow and says _____?   paw   peep

8. What gives milk and makes a _____ sound?   may   moo

9. What can you sit on that runs fast and makes a

   _____ sound?   neigh   need

10. What can see at night and says _____?   cool   whoo

11. What is soft and quiet and says _____?   mew   mow

12. What is cute and furry and _____?   beaks   barks

13. "I _____," I said. "It's a dog."   know   now

14. "No," he laughed. "It's a _____!"   south   seal

Sing Along

Take Care of Earth

The animals and seas,
The open space and trees,
Oh, yes! They're here to stay
If everyone agrees . . .

To . . .
Recycle and reuse—
It's up to us to choose.
We *must* take care of Earth!
Let's sing and spread the news.

▶ Name some things we should try to reuse or recycle.

THINK! Why is it important for everyone to help take care of our land, air, and water?

Home Letter

Dear Family,

Your child will want to share with you what we'll be learning in the next few weeks—to identify and use prefixes, suffixes, and base words. A prefix is a word part that comes before a base word, such as **un**like. A suffix is a word part that comes after a base word, such as like**able**. We'll also learn the rules for dividing words into syllables. As we practice these skills, we will learn why Earth's resources are important to us and how we can help take care of them.

At-Home Activities

Here are some activities you and your child might like to do together.

▶ Sing the song together. Talk about things you can do at home to help save resources.

▶ Create another verse to add to the song.

▶ Together, make a poster of How-To Tips including pictures and words that will help family members to be better caretakers of Earth's resources.

Book Corner

You and your child might enjoy reading these books together. Look for them in your local library.

When the Monkeys Came Back
by Kristine L. Franklin

After 56 years, Marta finally hears the howler monkeys in the Costa Rican forest she worked hard to restore after developers cut it down.

Squish! A Wetland Walk
by Nancy Luenn

In this poem, a father and son discover the importance of wetlands and the many types of animals that live there.

Sincerely,

Name _____

▶ **Read each word and write its base word on the line.**

1. displease _____

2. uncertain _____

3. disorder _____

4. misbehave _____

5. unfair _____

6. unhappy _____

7. dissatisfy _____

8. unfold _____

9. disagree _____

10. misfortune _____

11. mislay _____

12. unpleasant _____

13. disobey _____

14. unequal _____

15. discharge _____

16. uncover _____

17. misspell _____

18. discolor _____

19. disappear _____

20. unseen _____

21. misuse _____

22. mistake _____

23. untrue _____

24. disable _____

25. mistrust _____

26. uneven _____

27. dislike _____

28. unchain _____

Read each word and write its base word on the line.

1. unable _____

2. unpleasant _____

3. unhappy _____

4. unmade _____

5. disobey _____

6. misprint _____

7. dislike _____

8. displease _____

Read each sentence. Write a word from the examples above that means the same as the underlined words in the sentence.

9. Messy bedrooms <u>do not please</u> Susan's mother. _____

10. Susan's bed was <u>not made</u> yesterday morning. _____

11. Susan was <u>not able</u> to clean her room before school. _____

12. Her mom was <u>not happy</u> and asked Susan to clean it. _____

13. Susan would <u>not like</u> making her mother angry. _____

14. She cleaned the <u>not pleasant</u> mess. _____

15. Susan won't <u>not obey</u> her mother again. _____

Lesson 69
Prefixes un-, dis-, and mis-

With your child, look up words in the dictionary with the prefixes *un-*, *dis-*, and *mis-*.

Name _____

RULES

The prefix **re** usually means **do again.**
The prefix **de** usually means **from.** The prefix **ex** usually means **out of** or **from.**
Repaint means **paint again.**
Depart means **go away from.**
Export means **send out of.**

 Read each word and write its base word on the line.

1. declaw _____

2. reread _____

3. defrost _____

4. exchange _____

5. express _____

6. rebuild _____

7. refill _____

8. derail _____

9. reopen _____

10. rewrite _____

11. retrace _____

12. redo _____

13. reload _____

14. depart _____

15. rewash _____

16. dethrone _____

17. exclaim _____

18. detour _____

19. decode _____

20. export _____

21. refile _____

22. deplane _____

23. reteach _____

24. demerit _____

25. rewrap _____

26. reclaim _____

27. retie _____

28. decrease _____

Read each word and write its base word on the line.

1. disown _____

2. retell _____

3. unable _____

4. dishonest _____

5. mistake _____

6. exclaim _____

7. reopen _____

8. depart _____

Fill in the circle beside the word that completes each sentence. Write the word on the line.

9. Al _____ Marie's invitation.

○ reloaded
○ reread
○ refilled

10. He was _____ if he could go to the party.

○ unsure
○ unsaid
○ unsafe

11. He _____ ice cream and cake.

○ disagreed
○ disowned
○ disliked

12. He would go to the party, but he would _____ early.

○ defend
○ depart
○ defrost

13. At the party Marie _____ her gifts.

○ unchained
○ unloaded
○ unwrapped

14. She could hardly wait to _____ the bows.

○ untie
○ unpaid
○ untrue

15. Al decided to _____ his stay for a few hours.

○ explain
○ exhale
○ extend

Name _____

Read the definitions carefully. Then read each word below, and write its prefix, its base word, and its suffix in the correct columns.

DEFINITIONS

A **base word** is a word to which a prefix or a suffix may be added to form a new word. A **prefix** is added at the beginning of a base word. A **suffix** is added at the end of a base word.

re + turn = **re**turn
quick + **ly** = quick**ly**

prefix	base word	suffix

1. rebuilding _____ _____ _____

2. recovered _____ _____ _____

3. unkindly _____ _____ _____

4. uncomfortable _____ _____ _____

5. unhappiness _____ _____ _____

6. discovers _____ _____ _____

7. misbehaving _____ _____ _____

8. displeasing _____ _____ _____

9. unpacking _____ _____ _____

10. exclaiming _____ _____ _____

11. derailed _____ _____ _____

12. repainting _____ _____ _____

13. recycling _____ _____ _____

14. disagreeable _____ _____ _____

15. defrosting _____ _____ _____

Read each sentence. Use the code to make the two words under the sentence. Then circle the word that completes the sentence. Underline the prefix or suffix in each of the coded words.

1 = a	4 = e	7 = i	10 = m	13 = r	16 = u
2 = c	5 = f	8 = k	11 = n	14 = s	17 = w
3 = d	6 = h	9 = l	12 = p	15 = t	18 = y

1

Let's all try to be _____ caretakers of our planet!

— — — — — — — —   — — — — — — —
2 1 13 4 9 4 14 14   6 4 9 12 5 16 9

2

Try to _____ shopping bags and plastic containers.

— — — — — — —   — — — — —
3 7 14 9 7 8 4   13 4 16 14 4

3

Pick up _____ newspapers, bottles, and boxes and recycle them.

— — — — — —   — — — — — — — — —
8 7 11 3 9 18   16 11 2 9 1 7 10 4 3

4

Try not to be _____ when using water or electricity.

— — — — — — — —   — — — — — — — —
17 1 14 15 4 5 16 9   13 4 5 7 9 9 4 3

5

If people _____ say they cannot help, share these tips.

— — — — — —   — — — — — — — —
11 4 1 15 9 18   16 11 17 7 14 4 9 18

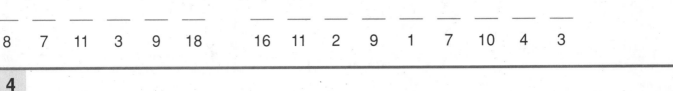

Lesson 71
Prefixes, base words, suffixes

Home Using the code on the page, ask your child to make up words for you to decode.

Name _____

▶ Divide each word into syllables. Remember to use hyphens.

1. rewrite _____

2. exchange _____

3. untie _____

4. dislike _____

5. unpaid _____

6. playing _____

7. spoonful _____

8. colder _____

9. softest _____

10. kindly _____

11. unsafely _____

12. repainted _____

13. distasteful _____

14. unhandy _____

15. mistrust _____

16. renew _____

17. displease _____

18. deplane _____

19. export _____

20. sleepless _____

21. boxes _____

22. dampness _____

23. rested _____

24. flying _____

25. unwisely _____

26. returning _____

27. unhealthy _____

28. retelling _____

29. replanted _____

30. unkindly _____

Divide the words into syllables, using hyphens.

1. playing _____
2. disclose _____
3. displease _____
4. spoonful _____
5. derail _____
6. rebuild _____
7. unload _____

8. loudest _____
9. softly _____
10. harmless _____
11. unkind _____
12. dislike _____
13. sweeten _____
14. repaint _____

Underline each word that has a prefix or a suffix. Write the word on the line, using hyphens to divide the word into syllables.

15. Vicky was careless with her gray coat. _____

16. She is unhappy because she lost it. _____

17. Now she needs a coat for the colder weather. _____

18. She is very uncomfortable in the cold wind. _____

19. Vicky's mom is displeased about the loss. _____

20. She tells Vicky to be more careful next time. _____

21. They will replace the lost coat on Monday. _____

22. Then Vicky will earn the money to repay Mom. _____

Ask your child to name the prefix or suffix and the base word in the story words.

Study each rule about dividing words into syllables.

dog-house   cat-house   bird-house   mouse-house

Divide each compound word into syllables. Remember to use hyphens.

1. into _____

2. doorman _____

3. birthday _____

4. cowboy _____

5. rainbow _____

6. inside _____

7. tiptoe _____

8. someone _____

9. sidewalk _____

10. sunshine _____

11. tonight _____

12. today _____

13. dishpan _____

14. highway _____

15. moonlight _____

16. bedtime _____

17. strawberry _____

18. headline _____

19. dustpan _____

20. hillside _____

21. sailboat _____

22. driveway _____

 **Phonics & Reading**

 Read the following passage.
Circle the compound words.

Downtown or Trash Town?

When is a city sidewalk like a trash can? When it has litter on it! Old newspapers, candy wrappers, soda cans, and other garbage make it look as though no one cares about the place. That is what has happened to this city's downtown. The ugly mess cannot be overlooked!

You can help your hometown. Organize a litter drive. Get everyone together to make a difference in a park or playground, uptown or downtown, or along the highway.

 **Phonics & Writing**

 Write a postcard to the mayor of your town and give three reasons why it is important to organize a litter drive. Use the words in the box.

Dear _____ :

_____

_____

_____

_____

_____

Sincerely,·

_____

playground
highway
newspapers
overrun
downtown
uptown

Lesson 73
Compound words: Reading, Writing

 Home

Ask your child to point out the compound words in the passage.

Name _____

► **Study the rule. Then divide each word into syllables. Remember to use hyphens.**

When a word has a suffix with a vowel sound in it, divide the word between the base word and the suffix.
kind-ness

1. saying _____

2. sharpen _____

3. boxful _____

4. cheated _____

5. making _____

6. planted _____

7. hardness _____

8. homeless _____

9. needed _____

10. walking _____

11. newest _____

12. flying _____

13. cupful _____

14. kindly _____

15. playing _____

16. quicker _____

17. foxes _____

18. sleeping _____

19. safely _____

20. gases _____

21. fearless _____

22. smallest _____

23. reading _____

24. gladly _____

25. helpless _____

26. healthful _____

27. rested _____

28. careless _____

29. colder _____

30. loudest _____

31. neatly _____

32. faster _____

> **Divide the words into syllables, using hyphens.**

1. painful _____
2. tallest _____
3. playful _____
4. scary _____
5. watching _____
6. sickness _____

7. smarter _____
8. darted _____
9. loudly _____
10. classes _____
11. interesting _____
12. singing _____

> **Read each sentence. Choose one of the words above to complete the sentence. Write it on the line.**

13. Two _____ from our school visited the zoo.

14. We enjoyed _____ the animals.

15. One _____ monkey chased another.

16. The birds were _____ joyfully.

17. A lion roared _____.

18. Otters _____ down a waterfall.

19. The alligator showed his _____ sharp teeth.

20. We learned many _____ facts.

21. The _____ animal is the giraffe.

22. The elephant is _____ than most animals.

162 Lesson 74
Words with suffixes: Syllables

Home Help your children use the words from numbers 1–12 in sentences.

Name _____

When a word has a prefix, divide the word between the prefix and the base word.

re-new

▶ **Study the rule. Then write each word, dividing it into syllables.**

1. unable _____

2. reread _____

3. distrust _____

4. recolor _____

5. depart _____

6. express _____

7. misprint _____

8. return _____

9. disown _____

10. untie _____

11. replace _____

12. exclaim _____

13. undress _____

14. deform _____

15. unkind _____

16. display _____

17. unpin _____

18. misfit _____

19. exchange _____

20. unfair _____

21. depress _____

22. displease _____

23. detour _____

24. unscrew _____

25. derail _____

26. renew _____

27. export _____

28. repaint _____

29. discharge _____

30. unfold _____

31. review _____

32. defrost _____

> **Divide the words into syllables using hyphens.**

1. unsafe _____
2. discomfort _____
3. repair _____
4. refund _____
5. remove _____

6. delay _____
7. depart _____
8. request _____
9. displease _____
10. unlock _____

> **Read each sentence. Choose one of the words above to complete the sentence. Write it on the line.**

11. Beth used a key to _____ the car.

12. She had to _____ her suitcase from the trunk.

13. She felt some _____ because of her heavy bag.

14. Beth had to _____ someone's help.

15. Her plane was to _____ soon for Boston.

16. There was a _____ in the flight.

17. The plane was _____ to travel in.

18. The mechanics could not _____ it.

19. Beth got a _____ on her ticket.

20. It did not _____ Beth that she missed her trip.

Lesson 75
Words with prefixes: Syllables

Home

Ask your child to name other words with prefixes to divide into syllables.

Name _____

When two or more consonants come between two vowels in a word, the word is usually divided between the first two consonants.

hun-gry

▶ **Study the rule. Then write each word, dividing it into syllables.**

1. picture _____
2. pencil _____
3. confess _____
4. goblin _____
5. forgave _____
6. basket _____
7. admire _____
8. princess _____
9. complete _____
10. mistake _____
11. candy _____
12. harbor _____
13. plenty _____
14. children _____
15. pilgrim _____

16. sudden _____
17. number _____
18. silver _____
19. Kansas _____
20. master _____
21. finger _____
22. invite _____
23. kidnap _____
24. doctor _____
25. riddle _____
26. almost _____
27. chapter _____
28. surprise _____
29. dictate _____
30. butter _____

> **Write each word, dividing it into syllables.**

1. magnet _____
2. sudden _____
3. blanket _____
4. plenty _____
5. invite _____
6. hungry _____

7. circus _____
8. confess _____
9. picnic _____
10. almost _____
11. puppy _____
12. bottom _____

> **Read each sentence. Choose one of the words from above to complete the sentence. Write it on the line.**

13. Meg took a delicious _____ to the park.

14. She laid the food on a _____.

15. She had _____ of food to eat.

16. There was a _____ tug on her pants.

17. A _____ was pulling it.

18. Meg _____ fell over.

19. The puppy was very _____, too.

20. Meg decided to _____ it to lunch.

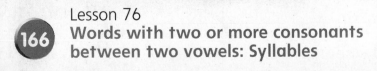

Lesson 76
166 **Words with two or more consonants between two vowels: Syllables**

Name _____

Read the rules. Write each word, dividing it into syllables. Then write the number of the rule that you used to help you.

RULES FOR SYLLABICATION

1. A one-syllable word is never divided.
2. Divide a compound word between the words that make up the compound word.
3. When a word has a suffix with a vowel sound in it, divide the word between the base word and the suffix.
4. When a word has a prefix, divide the word between the prefix and the base word.
5. When two or more consonants come between two vowels in a word, the word is usually divided between the first two consonants.

1. circus _____ ___

2. monkey _____ ___

3. donkey _____ ___

4. surprise _____ ___

5. homeless _____ ___

6. balloon _____ ___

7. smallest _____ ___

8. helping _____ ___

9. outdoors _____ ___

10. sudden _____ ___

11. later _____ ___

12. refresh _____ ___

13. quickly _____ ___

14. hungry _____ ___

15. hardness _____ ___

16. displease _____ ___

17. slowly _____ ___

18. safe _____ ___

19. curtain _____ ___

20. harmful _____ ___

21. backyard _____ ___

22. churches _____ ___

23. railroad _____ ___

24. airplane _____ ___

> **Read each sentence. Circle the word that will complete it. Write the correct word, dividing it into syllables on the line.**

1. Joe and I like to _____ at pictures.
   look   pilgrim   tiptoe

2. We sit out in the _____.
   churches   backyard   displease

3. Joe turns the pages very _____.
   ballroom   harming   slowly

4. Here is my sister's second birthday _____.
   bottom   party   walnut

5. It was fun to watch her _____ her presents.
   chimney   unwrap   homeless

6. Here she is blowing out the _____ on her cake.
   hamburger   candles   cards

7. There is my _____, Goofy.
   puppy   shallow   walnut

8. That's a _____ at the zoo.
   tiptoe   monkey   smallest

9. Let's take some more _____ soon!
   quickly   harness   pictures

THINK! Why does Joe turn the pages slowly?

Lesson 77
**Review syllabication rules:
Words in context**

Home

With your child, divide all the answer choice words into syllables.

Name _____

When a single consonant comes between two vowels in a word, the word is usually divided after the consonant if the first vowel is short.

lem-on

▶ **Read the rule. Then write each word, dividing it into syllables.**

1. robin _____

2. cabin _____

3. figure _____

4. wagon _____

5. travel _____

6. palace _____

7. statue _____

8. finish _____

9. river _____

10. clever _____

11. magic _____

12. visit _____

13. shadow _____

14. model _____

15. dragon _____

▶ **Write a story about the picture using as many of the above words as you can.**

_____

_____

_____

_____

_____

Lesson 7.8
Syllables in v-c-v words
169

▶ **Write each word, dividing it into syllables.**

1. cabin _____

2. travel _____

3. magic _____

4. visit _____

5. figure _____

6. palace _____

7. ever _____

8. river _____

9. wagon _____

10. dragon _____

▶ **Read each sentence. Choose one of the words from above to complete the sentence. Write it on the line.**

11. There once lived a large green _____.

12. He lived in a tiny log _____.

13. He liked to _____ to many places.

14. One day he rode away in his red _____.

15. When he got to a _____, he swam across.

16. He came to the royal _____.

17. "I think I shall _____ the king," he said.

18. "I'll do some _____ tricks for him."

19. The king could not _____ out how the tricks were done.

20. He wondered if the dragon would _____ visit him again.

Name _____

> **Study the rule. Then write each word, dividing it into syllables.**

When a single consonant comes between two vowels in a word, the word is usually divided before the consonant if the first vowel is long.

ti-ny

1. lilac _____
2. polar _____
3. spider _____
4. frozen _____
5. moment _____
6. lazy _____
7. pupil _____
8. lady _____
9. pirate _____

10. pilot _____
11. cozy _____
12. motel _____
13. David _____
14. music _____
15. tiger _____
16. broken _____
17. famous _____
18. paper _____

> **Write a sentence using as many of the above words as you can.**

_____

_____

_____

_____

> **Write each word, dividing it into syllables.**

1. paper _____
2. frozen _____
3. lilac _____
4. cozy _____
5. music _____
6. policeman _____
7. spider _____
8. pony _____
9. sofa _____
10. lazy _____

> **Read each sentence. Choose a word from above to complete the sentence. Write it on the line.**

11. A _____ gave us directions to the park.

12. A band was playing _____.

13. First we went on the _____ rides.

14. Then we bought _____ ice cream.

15. We sat by a _____ bush to rest.

16. There we saw a _____ spinning a web.

17. When I got home, I lay down on the _____.

18. It was so warm and _____ that I fell asleep.

Name _____

Study the rule. Read each word and circle the vowel that is sounded by itself. Then write each word, dividing it into syllables.

When a vowel is sounded alone in a word, it forms a syllable by itself.
pyr-a-mid

1. magazine _____

2. open _____

3. uniform _____

4. disagree _____

5. ahead _____

6. Canada _____

7. unit _____

8. telephone _____

9. disobey _____

10. alive _____

11. ocean _____

12. electric _____

13. against _____

14. document _____

15. gasoline _____

16. Mexico _____

17. eternal _____

18. monument _____

19. odor _____

20. ago _____

Write a postcard about a vacation using as many of the above words as you can.

_____

_____

_____

_____

_____

Read each sentence. Choose a word from the box to complete the sentence. Write it on the line.

1. Tory's family went to _____.

2. Every day they swam in the _____.

3. The marketplace was _____.

4. Many _____ were for sale.

5. Tory brought a _____ to read.

6. The family climbed a huge _____.

7. It had been built a long time _____.

8. A man in a _____ explained its history.

9. Tory ran down the steps _____ of her parents.

10. Then she wanted to run up the steps _____!

pyramid
magazine
uniform
items
ahead
ocean
again
ago
open
Mexico

Write the words from above, dividing them into syllables.

11. _____   16. _____

12. _____   17. _____

13. _____   18. _____

14. _____   19. _____

15. _____   20. _____

Lesson 80
Words with a vowel sounded alone: Syllabication

Using the words in the box, help your child write a new story.

Name _____

RULE 9

When two vowels come together in a word and are sounded separately, divide the word between the two vowels.

flu-id

▶ **Study the rule. Then write each word, dividing it into syllables.**

1. giant _____

2. polio _____

3. rodeo _____

4. radiator _____

5. graduate _____

6. dial _____

7. usual _____

8. science _____

9. poem _____

10. radio _____

11. lion _____

12. diet _____

13. ruin _____

14. cruel _____

15. pioneer _____

16. poet _____

17. create _____

18. idea _____

19. gradual _____

20. oriole _____

▶ **Write two sentences using as many of the above words as you can.**

_____

_____

_____

_____

Words with two vowels together that are sounded separately: Syllables

Write each word, dividing it into syllables.

1. radio _____
2. piano _____
3. diet _____
4. diaper _____
5. quiet _____
6. cruel _____
7. graduate _____
8. poem _____
9. lion _____
10. violin _____
11. violet _____
12. giant _____
13. guardian _____
14. create _____
15. rodeo _____

16. dandelion _____
17. Ohio _____
18. science _____
19. idea _____
20. denial _____
21. radiator _____
22. fluid _____
23. ruin _____
24. trial _____
25. theater _____
26. pioneer _____
27. hyena _____
28. period _____
29. realize _____
30. annual _____

Words with two vowels together that are sounded separately: Syllables

Home

Ask your child how he or she knew where to divide the words above into syllables.

Name _____

RULE 10

When a word ends in **le** preceded by a consonant, divide the word before that consonant.

nim-ble

▶ **Study the rule. Then write each word, dividing it into syllables.**

1. turtle _____

2. puzzle _____

3. gentle _____

4. whistle _____

5. eagle _____

6. maple _____

7. pebble _____

8. simple _____

9. thistle _____

10. circle _____

11. purple _____

12. bicycle _____

13. needle _____

14. riddle _____

15. people _____

16. rattle _____

17. scramble _____

18. cradle _____

19. dimple _____

20. sample _____

21. thimble _____

22. temple _____

23. tattle _____

24. middle _____

▶ **Write a short paragraph using as many of the above words as you can.**

_____

_____

_____

A Day at the Lake

One day, Mary and her dad rode their bicycles to a small lake. They parked the bikes under a maple tree and headed for the boat dock. A gentle breeze made the water ripple.

"I'll show you how to handle a canoe," said Dad. "It's simple. You'll be able to do it in no time."

The man at the dock untied a dark purple canoe and held it against the dock. Mary and her dad stepped squarely into the middle of the canoe so it wouldn't topple.

"You're very nimble," said Dad.

Mary's dad showed her how to use the paddle as a rudder at the end of each stroke to keep the canoe from going in a circle.

Then Mary tried it.

"You must have strong muscles," Dad said. "You are really doing well."

Mary was proud. She had learned to manage a canoe without any trouble.

1. _____   2. _____   3. _____

4. _____   5. _____   6. _____

7. _____   8. _____   9. _____

10. _____ 11. _____ 12. _____

13. _____ 14. _____ 15. _____

THINK! **Will Mary and her dad go canoeing again? Why do you think so?**

178 Lesson 82
Words with le: Syllables

Phonics & Spelling

▶ Say and spell each word. Write the word under the heading where it belongs.

Word List

bicycle	comfortable	defrost
discovered	frozen	magic
middle	misbehaves	open
pioneer	purple	rebuilding
science	unkindly	wagon

Words With Prefixes or Suffixes

_____

_____

_____

_____

_____

Words With Final le

_____

_____

_____

Two Vowels Together Sounded Separately

_____

_____

One Consonant Between Two Vowels

_____

_____

_____

Review prefixes, base words, suffixes, syllables: Spelling

Phonics & Writing

Write a letter to the editor of your local newspaper. Tell why people in your city or town should take good care of Earth. Use the model below to get started. Use some of the words in the box.

bicycle	highway	outdoors	rebuilding
comfortable	middle	planet	science
discovered	open	purple	unkindly

Date _____

Dear _____,

_____

_____

_____

_____

_____

_____

Sincerely,

_____

Book Corner

Rachel Carson: Writer and Scientist
by Carol Alexander

This book, part of the Beginning Biographies series, presents the life of the scientist and writer Rachel Carson. She was a pioneer in raising awareness about the importance of caring for our environment.

Ask your child to read you the letter he or she wrote.

Name _____

MARIO'S SCIENCE PROJECT

Mario was discouraged. He was uncertain what to do for his school science project. Suddenly, the wind blew a paper he was carrying out of his hand. As he recovered it, he noticed lots of paper on the sidewalk.

—FOLD—

—FOLD—

When Mario got home from the recycling center, he told his mother how discouraged he was. Mario's mother handed him some photos. They all showed Mario cleaning up the neighborhood.

"Here is your science project!" his mother exclaimed.

TALK ABOUT IT

What is Mario's science project? Do you think it is a good one? Why or why not?

Lesson 84

Prefixes, base words, suffixes, syllables: Take-Home Book

181

2

From a window, Mario's mother saw him picking up papers. "If there is one thing I really dislike, it's trash, but I'm still unsure about my science project," Mario said thoughtfully.

— FOLD —

— FOLD —

Mario picked up papers and cans on the street every day. He took them by the wagonful to a recycling center. But Mario was still doubtful about his science project.

3

TO CITY RECYCLING PLANT

Lesson 84
Prefixes, base words, suffixes, syllables: Take-Home Book

UNIT 6 CHECKUP

▶ Read each clue. Fill in the circle next to the prefix or suffix that will make a new word that matches the clue. Write the new word on the line.

1. <u>use</u> again   _____   ○ re-   ○ -ful   ○ mis-

2. not <u>usual</u>   _____   ○ -ly   ○ un-   ○ re-

3. <u>behaves</u> badly   _____   ○ mis-   ○ un-   ○ de-

4. giving <u>help</u>   _____   ○ -ful   ○ -ly   ○ ex-

5. not <u>pleased</u>   _____   ○ re-   ○ ex-   ○ dis-

6. to take away the <u>frost</u> _____ ○ un-   ○ de-   ○ -ly

▶ Read each word. Then fill in the circle beside the word that shows how to divide the word into syllables.

7. earth   ○ ear-th   ○ earth   ○ e-arth

8. sunset   ○ suns-et   ○ sunset   ○ sun-set

9. replanted   ○ re-plant-ed   ○ rep-lant-ed ○ replant-ed

10. better   ○ be-tter   ○ bett-er   ○ bet-ter

11. robin   ○ rob-in   ○ ro-bin   ○ ro-bi-n

12. magic   ○ mag-ic   ○ ma-gic   ○ magi-c

13. quiet   ○ qu-i-et   ○ quie-t   ○ qui-et

14. monument   ○ mo-nu-ment   ○ mon-u-ment   ○ monu-ment

15. purple   ○ pu-rple   ○ purp-le   ○ pur-ple

Read each sentence. Circle the word or words with a prefix or suffix.

1. News about Earth may displease you.

2. We cannot always rebuild what we have destroyed.

3. We cannot exchange dirty water for clean water overnight.

4. We know that the future of many kinds of animals is uncertain.

5. Many people do treat Earth and living things unkindly.

6. However, many more people are thoughtful.

7. Many people work hard for a comfortable, safe planet.

8. Earth can renew itself.

9. We must be hopeful about the future.

10. You can make a difference by pitching in to do your part!

Write the base word of each word you circled.

11. _____   12. _____

13. _____   14. _____

15. _____   16. _____

17. _____   18. _____

19. _____   20. _____

Sing Along

Getting to know me,
Getting to know all about me!

Getting to know me,
Getting to know who I am!

Getting to know me—
might be quite easy,
If I can see what sets me apart
Makes me, ME from the start—
A special ME!

▶ **What is it about you that sets you apart from everyone else?**

THINK! In what ways is everyone special?

Home Letter

Dear Family,

In this unit your child will be learning about synonyms (big-large, for example), antonyms (lost-found), homonyms (right-write), and homographs (such as play, which has several meanings). We will also be working on dictionary skills. As we explore these skills, we will learn about self-expression.

play

play

At-Home Activities

Here are some activities you and your child might like to do together.

▶ Write your child's name vertically on a piece of paper. Then have your child think of words beginning with the letters in his or her name to describe why he or she is a special person.

▶ Help your child make a word and picture montage that tells something about him- or herself. The montage might include family snapshots, pictures cut from old magazines, and words cut from newspaper headlines and advertisements.

Book Corner

You and your child might enjoy reading these books together. Look for them in your local library.

Guess Who My Favorite Person Is
by Byrd Baylor

Two friends meet in an alfalfa field and spend the afternoon guessing each other's favorite things.

Jacques-Henri Lartigue: Boy with a Camera
by John Cech

This photo essay features photographs that Lartigue took as a child and his creativity, excitement and joy in taking them.

Sincerely,

Name _____

DEFINITION
Synonyms are words that have the same or almost the same meaning.
big—large   fall—drop

▶ **Read each sentence. Then rewrite it, replacing the underlined word with a synonym from the box.**

closes	discovers	field	forgets	glad
happens	loud	pretty	radio	silent
tale	teaches	unhappy	upset	woods

1. My dad enjoys reading me a <u>story</u> before bedtime. _____

_____

2. I am <u>happy</u> when we spend time together. _____

_____

3. He begins to read when I am <u>quiet</u>. _____

_____

4. He always <u>finds</u> a new story to read. _____

_____

5. This story is about a girl who lives in the <u>forest</u>. _____

_____

6. She wears a <u>beautiful</u> red cape. _____

_____

7. I can't wait to find out what <u>occurs</u>. _____

_____

THINK! **What story do you think the girl's dad read to her? How can you tell?**

Read each riddle. Write a word from the box to answer the riddle.

big   beautiful   boat   close   funny   hear   woods

1. I have four letters. I mean the same as <u>listen</u>.   I am _____.

2. I have five letters. I mean the same as <u>comical</u>.   I am _____.

3. I have four letters. I mean the same as <u>ship</u>.   I am _____.

4. I have five letters. I mean the same as <u>near</u>.   I am _____.

5. I have three letters. I mean the same as <u>large</u>.   I am _____.

6. I have five letters. I mean the same as <u>forest</u>.   I am _____.

7. I have nine letters. I mean the same as <u>pretty</u>.   I am _____.

For each group of words, draw a line from the word in the first column to its synonym in the second column.

8		**9**		**10**	
fix	hurt	huge	said	say	drop
injure	gift	pretty	large	fall	little
present	repair	told	quiet	glisten	even
raise	remain	silent	glad	level	tell
stay	lift	happy	beautiful	small	sparkle

11		**12**		**13**	
fearful	crawl	handsome	attractive	powerful	trip
reap	sad	swift	dreary	strike	piece
creep	afraid	gloomy	marvelous	journey	strong
big	gather	wonderful	informed	store	hit
unhappy	large	reported	speedy	part	shop

Lesson 86
Synonyms

Home

Ask your child to read riddles 1–7 for you to answer.

Name _____

▶ For each group of words, draw a line from the word in the first column to its antonym in the second column.

DEFINITION

Antonyms are words that are opposite or almost opposite in meaning.

lost—found

1		**2**		**3**	
strong	dark	light	tight	large	fearful
hot	cold	loose	warm	sharp	dull
many	few	cool	heavy	sick	healthy
light	weak	fat	thin	fearless	small
4		**5**		**6**	
asleep	fast	swiftly	quiet	hard	under
slow	awake	noisy	slowly	young	soft
friend	enemy	difficult	go	descend	old
full	empty	come	easy	over	climb

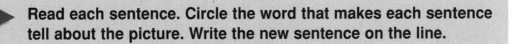

▶ Read each sentence. Circle the word that makes each sentence tell about the picture. Write the new sentence on the line.

7. Danny and Fran (climbed,   descended) a hill.

_____

8. It was (easy,   difficult) to go up the steep hill.

_____

9. Along the path, they saw many (dull,   sharp) rocks.

_____

10. When they reached the top, they were (happy,   sad).

_____

Lesson 87
Antonyms

189

Read each word. Write its antonym in the blanks. Write the letters from the boxes to answer the question.

above	clear	enemy	healthy	loose	outside
over	separates	sharp	simple	tall	wide

1. tight ___ ___ ☐ ___ ___

2. friend ___ ___ ___ ___ ___

3. joins ___ ___ ☐ ___ ___ ___ ___ ___

4. difficult ___ ___ ☐ ___ ___

5. under ☐ ___ ___ ___

6. inside ___ ___ ☐ ___ ___ ___

7. smoky ___ ___ ___ ___ ___

8. narrow ___ ☐ ___ ___

9. short ☐ ___ ___ ___

10. sick ___ ☐ ___ ___ ___ ___ ___

11. below ___ ___ ___ ___

12. dull ☐ ___ ___ ___ ___

What are antonyms? _____

Ask your child to name other antonym pairs and explain their meanings.

Name _____

DEFINITION

Homonyms are words that sound alike but have different spellings and meanings.

right—write

1. My soccer team (beat, beet) every team this year. _____

2. We (maid, made) it to the city finals. _____

3. We (road, rode) to the big game in a bus. _____

4. We wore our new (blew, blue) uniforms. _____

5. "Play (fair, fare)," said our coach. _____

6. Then he (sent, cent) us out onto the field. _____

7. The time went (buy, by) fast. _____

8. We (eight, ate) oranges at half time. _____

9. We couldn't (wait, weight) to continue the game. _____

10. The game lasted one (our, hour). _____

11. Katie's goal (won, one) the game for us. _____

12. The team's picture will (bee, be) in the newspaper. _____

13. Our trophy will arrive next (weak, week). _____

THINK! How do you think the team will feel about playing together next year?

Lesson 88
Homonyms

191

Read each sentence. Circle the word that completes the sentence. Write it on the line.

1. _____ have a favorite hobby.   Eye   I

2. I like to _____ with my brother.   sail   sale

3. He _____ many things about boats.   nose   knows

4. He is teaching me to tie a square _____.   knot   not

5. Last week he _____ me practice.   maid   made

6. I still can't tie it the _____ way.   right   write

7. We sail _____ boat every weekend.   hour   our

8. We will sail today _____ tomorrow.   oar   or

9. We must _____ for the wind to blow.   wait   weight

For each group of words, draw a line from the word in the first column to its homonym in the second column.

10		**11**	
break	knot	ate	wrap
not	stake	ring	wring
weight	wait	rap	eight
steak	brake	bare	bear

12		**13**	
right	dye	I	pane
see	sea	led	sale
die	road	sail	eye
rode	write	pain	lead

Home

Ask your child to choose a word pair in each set and explain the meanings.

Name _____

 Read the passage. Then write a homonym from the passage to complete each sentence.

MEET ADAM BARATZ

Software companies often write to Adam Baratz. They want to know what he thinks of their products. Adam checks to be sure a company's program works right. Is Adam a computer scientist? No, he is not even a grown-up. Adam is just nine years old, but he is the president of his own company, Adam's Beta Testers.

This computer whiz spends one to two hours a day at his computer. His latest computer is his fourth one. His last one was too slow for the computer programs he uses. To learn even more about computers, Adam goes to computer camp for eight weeks in the summer.

Adam hasn't made any money from his work. But he doesn't have to buy computer software—he gets it for free!

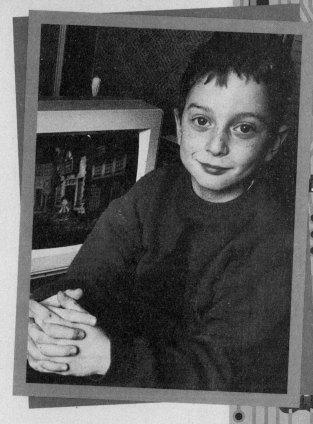

1. Software companies _____ to Adam Baratz.

2. They _____ he can help them.

3. Adam checks to be sure their programs work _____.

4. Adam spends _____ weeks at computer camp.

5. Adam hasn't _____ any money from his work.

6. But he doesn't have to _____ computer software!

 Why do software companies ask Adam Baratz for help?

Lesson 89
Review homonyms: Reading

What do you do that's special? Write an article to tell people about yourself. Use the words in the word box.

be	eye	I	see	our	sew	write
four	right	wear	build	hour	sea	where

_____

_____

_____

_____

_____

_____

_____

_____

194 Lesson 89
Review homonyms: Writing

Ask your child to read his or her article and name the homonyms.

Name _____

▶ **Read the hint. Then write each list of words in alphabetical order.**

HINT

Words in a dictionary are listed in alphabetical order. If the first letters of the words are the same, look at the second letter. If the first two letters are the same, look at the third letter.

1

f̲oxes _____

g̲oat _____

b̲eaver _____

c̲amel _____

d̲eer _____

a̲ntelope _____

e̲lephant _____

2

D̲anny _____

A̲nn _____

F̲rank _____

C̲arl _____

B̲etty _____

E̲llen _____

G̲erry _____

3

b̲i̲cycle _____

ba̲t _____

bu̲bbles _____

bl̲ocks _____

bo̲at _____

br̲eak _____

4

ch̲e̲ese _____

ch̲o̲p _____

ch̲r̲ome _____

ch̲a̲ir _____

ch̲i̲ldren _____

ch̲u̲ckle _____

Look at each pair of guide words and the words below them. Circle the words in each list that you would find on a page with those guide words.

1	**mice • mop**	2	**fish • gate**	3	**dance • day**
	mile		five		dark
	men		frogs		deer
	mitt		girl		doll
	moon		gave		date
	mask		fun		dawn

4	**rabbit • rake**	5	**wagon • wax**	6	**present • print**
	radio		wallet		pretzel
	raccoon		wooden		princess
	rocket		watching		propeller
	radish		watermelon		principal
	rain		whale		press

Home Name a word. Ask your child where the word could be found in the dictionary.

Look at each pair of guide words. Write the word from the sandwich that belongs between the guide words.

1. sailboat _____ saw

2. dragon _____ dressing

3. flat _____ flute

4. jacket _____ jay

5. ladder _____ lazy

6. record _____ red

7. think _____ thorn

8. camel _____ candy

9. whiskers _____ wishbone

10. dazzle _____ dear

11. zebra _____ zigzag

12. rabbit _____ raffle

candle
deal
drapes
flowers
jar
lantern
race
rectangle
sandwiches
thirteen
window
zero

Look at each pair of guide words and the dictionary page number. Write the page number on which you would find each word listed below.

each • elevator 210	**elf • escape** 215	**fake • frown** 243
13. elephant _____	14. favorite _____	15. erase _____
16. easel _____	17. English _____	18. farmer _____
19. family _____	20. educate _____	21. eggplant _____

Read each pair of guide words. Circle the four words in the box that would appear between those guide words. Then write the words you circled in alphabetical order on the lines.

1

can • cave

candy
case
cold
carton
cap

_____
_____
_____
_____

2

hide • hit

hen
hilly
hiker
hip
himself

_____
_____
_____
_____

3

sad • saw

same
soap
save
sand
sail

_____
_____
_____
_____

4

train • truck

treetop
trap
trot
tail
tray

_____
_____
_____
_____

Name _____

HINT

Dictionary words are listed in alphabetical order. You can find a word quickly if you think of the dictionary as having three parts: **Beginning Letters** (A-I), **Middle Letters** (J-Q), and **Ending Letters** (R-Z).

► **Where in the dictionary would you find the words in the box? Write each word where it belongs.**

aunt	sister	doctor	myself	father
joy	love	teacher	family	write
read	brother	mother	uncle	neighbor

Beginning (A-I)	Middle (J-Q)	End (R-Z)
1. _____	2. _____	3. _____
4. _____	5. _____	6. _____
7. _____	8. _____	9. _____
10. _____	11. _____	12. _____
13. _____	14. _____	15. _____

► **Write Beginning, Middle, or End to tell where in the dictionary each word in bold print can be found.**

16. People **express** themselves in different ways. _____

17. Some people **write** books or poetry. _____

18. Others create works of **art**. _____

19. Athletes **play** many different sports. _____

20. Dancers express themselves with their **bodies**. _____

21. How do you express **yourself**? _____

Lesson 92
Locating words in the dictionary   199

> **Read the information in each exercise. Then answer the questions. Use page 199 to help you.**

1

You are writing a science report on dinosaurs.
Look up the word <u>Tyrannosaurus</u>. In which section
of the dictionary would you find this word? _____

You open the dictionary and see the guide words
unbroken • undergo. Would *Tyrannosaurus*
come **before, on,** or **after** a page with those
guide words? _____

2

While reading a recipe, you see the word <u>barbecue</u>.
Where in the dictionary will you find this word? _____

You open the dictionary and see the guide words
by • category. Would *barbecue* come **before, on,**
or **after** a page with those guide words? _____

3

In a book of old Roman myths, you see the word
<u>Jupiter</u>. In which section of the dictionary should
you look to find this word? _____

You open the dictionary and see the guide words
jump • justice. Would *Jupiter* come **before, on,**
or **after** a page with those guide words? _____

4

You want to know more about the continent. Look
up <u>North America</u>. In which section of the dictionary
would you find these words? _____

You open the dictionary and see the guide words
music • nap. Would *North America* come **before,
on,** or **after** a page with those guide words? _____

Discuss your child's answers to
questions 1–4.

Name _____

Look at each picture. Read the dictionary entries next to it. In the box, write the number of the entry whose definition goes with the picture.

1

loaf[1]   a portion of bread or cake baked in a definite form

loaf[2]   to idle away time

2

bat-ter[1]   to beat very hard

bat-ter[2]   a thick mixture of flour, milk, or water, and eggs beaten together for use in cooking

bat-ter[3]   a person who bats, in baseball or cricket

3

mole[1]   a small spot on the skin, usually dark and slightly raised

mole[2]   a small furry animal with poor eyesight that lives underground

4

scale[1]   one of the thin, flat plates that covers the body of certain animals

scale[2]   a device for weighing

scale[3]   (in music) a series of tones either going up or going down

1

prune¹   a variety of plum that dries without spoiling

prune²   to cut off or trim twigs or branches

Grandpa will <u>prune</u> the bushes in his garden.

2

fine¹   very good

fine²   money paid as a penalty for breaking a law

Meg did a <u>fine</u> job of painting the book shelves.

3

spoke¹   the past tense of **speak**

spoke²   a bar coming out of the hub of a wheel

Danny had to repair two of the <u>spokes</u> on his bike.

4

bat¹   a wooden club used to hit a ball, as in baseball or cricket

bat²   a flying mammal, active at night

As they entered the cave, a <u>bat</u> flew out.

5

ring¹   a circular band worn on the finger as an ornament

ring²   to give forth a clear sound, as a doorbell or telephone bell

The bride and groom wore matching gold <u>rings</u>.

6

case¹   a situation or condition, as in *a sad case*

case²   a container

Janet put her new pin in her jewelry <u>case</u>.

7

post¹   an upright piece of timber or metal

post²   a position to which a person is assigned

Claude hammered the fence <u>post</u> into the ground.

8

mail¹   letters or packages that are delivered by the post office

mail²   armor made of metal rings linked together

Fran got <u>mail</u> from her pen pal in Australia.

202

Lesson 93
Multiple meanings (homographs)

Help your child think of a sentence using the other meaning in each set.

Name _____

Phonics & Spelling

▶ **Find the synonym in the box for each word.**
Write it on the line.

Word List (display   find   quick   raise)

1. show _____   2. locate _____

3. swift _____   4. lift _____

▶ **Find the antonym in the box for each word.**
Write it on the line.

Word List (come   high   light   something)

5. nothing _____   6. low _____

7. heavy _____   8. go _____

▶ **Write a homonym for each word.**

9. right _____   10. buy _____

11. dear _____   12. stare _____

Phonics & Writing

Write a computer E-mail message to someone whom you admire. Tell your hero something about yourself that may interest her or him. Use some of your spelling words.

COMPOSE MAIL

TO:

SUBJECT:

MESSAGE:

display
here
high
like
low
new
old
right
show
week
well
write

Book Corner

A First Clay Gathering
by Nora Navanjo-Morse

A young girl from the Tewa Pueblo in New Mexico gathers clay to make her first piece of pottery.

Name _____

The Remembering QUILT

Bea's grandmother was sewing a quilt. Each square told a story about Bea's family. Some of the cloth Grandma used was new, and some was very old.

"Where did this pretty blue square come from, Grandma?" asked Bea.

"This is from the dress I wore the day I met your grandfather," Grandma said.

FOLD   FOLD

Grandma tucked the quilt around Bea and held her in her warm arms.

"Whenever you feel cold, you can wrap the quilt around you," she said.

"And when I'm wrapped in the quilt, I'll remember our family," said Bea. "The remembering quilt won't let me forget."

TALK ABOUT IT

How can the quilt help Bea remember her family?

4

Review synonyms, antonyms, homonyms: Take-Home Book

"Tell me about this square," said Bea.

"This tells how my great-great-grandparents came here by boat," Grandma said. "It was a long, hard trip across the blue sea. They shed many tears when they left their home."

"It wasn't right to take them when they didn't want to go, was it?" asked Bea.

"No," said Grandma. "People know that now, but it was a long time ago."

FOLD

FOLD

Grandma told Bea the story of each square in the quilt. Her fingers moved quickly as she sewed the blocks together. She stitched more slowly as she sewed a bee on one square.

"Can you guess who this bee is supposed to be?" Grandma asked.

"It's me!" cried Bea. "What am I doing on the quilt?"

"Growing like the flowers in our garden," said Grandma. "Growing bigger every hour!"

Lesson 95
Review synonyms, antonyms, homonyms: Take-Home Book

UNIT 7 CHECKUP

Name _____

▶ Read each pair of words. Decide whether they are synonyms, antonyms, or homonyms. Fill in the circle.

	Synonyms	Antonyms	Homonyms
1. right/write	○	○	○
2. right/wrong	○	○	○
3. display/show	○	○	○
4. high/low	○	○	○
5. here/hear	○	○	○

▶ Read the word. Fill in the circle beside the guide words under which the entry word would be listed.

6. diet	○ dig-dip	○ debt-dent	○ did-different
7. ramp	○ ran-rap	○ rake-rang	○ rabbit-rag
8. custom	○ cost-cup	○ cup-cut	○ come-couple
9. ocean	○ oar-odor	○ ouch-over	○ one-opera
10. limb	○ lick-like	○ list-little	○ lima-lint

▶ Write the words in the box in alphabetical order.

11. _____

12. _____

13. _____

14. _____

15. _____

16. _____

> display
> detract
> decide
> distance
> determine
> demand

Synonyms, antonyms, homonyms, dictionary skills: Checkup

Read the sentence. Choose the meaning of the word that is used in the sentence. Write the number of the meaning beside the sentence.

scale¹	one of the thin, flat plates that cover the body of certain animals
scale²	a device for weighing
scale³	(in music) a series of tones either going up or going down
spoke¹	the past tense of speak
spoke²	a bar coming out of the hub of a wheel
batter¹	a thick mixture of flour, milk, or water, and eggs beaten together for use in cooking
batter²	a person who bats, in baseball or cricket
fine¹	very good
fine²	money paid as a penalty for breaking a law

_____ 1. Amy mixed the **batter** for a surprise birthday cake.

_____ 2. Jason **spoke** to his class about his favorite hobby.

_____ 3. Mrs. Hadley paid a **fine** when her parking meter ran out.

_____ 4. The school nurse weighed pupils on a new **scale**.

Circle the word that finishes each sentence.

5. There is (no, know) person exactly like you.

6. You may like (to, too) play ball or swim.

7. Do you like the color (blew, blue)?

8. What day of the (weak, week) is your favorite?

9. Do you have a favorite poem or (tail, tale)?

10. What kind of music do you like to (here, hear)?

11. Do you like to play (team, teem) sports?

12. (Wear, Where) is your favorite place to visit?

Lesson 96
Synonyms, antonyms, homonyms, dictionary skills: Checkup